# MAKING
## *Friends*
### with PAIN

# MAKING *Friends* with PAIN

## LEARNING TO LIVE WELL WITH CHRONIC ILLNESS

*by Elizabeth Flora*

SADIE BOOKS

ST. LOUIS, MISSOURI

# ~ ACKNOWLEDGEMENTS ~

To Anne & Sam, my parents and friends, for all their love and support. I love and respect you more than words can express.

To Kelly, who has managed chronic illness most of her life. Hers is the shining example I try to follow. Kel, you are my hero.

To Dr. Sarah Kim Margolis, who never doubted that my pain was real.

To my physical therapist Dan Kelley, who started me on the right path.

To the many friends I cannot list here, whose love sustains me.

Most of all, I would like to thank God, for giving me the strength to face my challenges each day, and for reminding me that life is indeed worth living well.

# ~ DEDICATION ~

To Harry James Cargas, PhD.

My mentor and friend, who always encouraged me
to do more than I thought I could.
The world is a better place for having known him,
and I was richly blessed to have him in my life.

*In loving memory of Dr. Harry James Cargas, ten percent of the proceeds
from this book will be donated to the Holocaust Studies Fund,
c/o Webster University, Saint Louis, Missouri.*

# INTRODUCTION

This book is about learning to live well with chronic illness. What qualifies me to write such a book? I am not a doctor, nor could I be considered an expert on pain. I am a patient who has recently been diagnosed with Fibromyalgia Syndrome (FMS). I have had to learn to live with the daily challenges of chronic illness. To accept them as part of my life.

I will share my experience with you. The good, the bad, and the just plain ugly. Through it all, I have made friends with my pain and, in the process, found peace. You can, too. The goal is simple: learn to live well *with* pain, rather than *in spite of* it. Reaching this objective, however, is far from easy.

It's important to tell you now - this is *not* a book about Fibromyalgia. While FMS is one of the most common causes of chronic pain, there are many others. If you are looking for information on FMS, I recommend *The Fibromyalgia Help Book: Practical Guide to Living Better with Fibromyalgia* (Smith House Press 1996). It explains the disorder in clear, simple language, and includes suggestions I have found helpful for managing the illness.

Since my diagnosis, I have conducted a great deal of research on living with chronic illness. Through this process I made an interesting discovery. There are many books available on the subject, most written by doctors and health care professionals. They provide practical, scientific information on the how, why and what of chronic illness. None explored the *emotions* of the patient. Some touched on the subject, but most merely scratched the surface.

These books did not prepare me for the emotional impact of chronic illness. I was overwhelmed many times by the strength of my feelings; I didn't realize they were a normal reaction to the diagnosis of a chronic illness. No one told me what to expect. Whether you are a patient, a friend, or a family member of someone affected by chronic illness, you need to know how it will impact your life.

Many people feel that if a health condition is not life threatening, it is not serious. You know this is not true. Having a chronic illness is serious to *you*. It changes everything. Adjusting to those changes is one of the most difficult challenges you'll ever face. It will be with you every single day for the rest of your life.

Expect to struggle as you come to terms with this harsh reality. Initially, you may be intimidated and feel overwhelmed. However, you *will* prevail. There *is* hope. Your life is altered, but you can expect to experience joy again if you accept the necessary changes and losses.

At times I wanted to die, because death would bring an end to my pain. Faced with great pain day in and day out, I simply could not fathom how I would make it. I was clawing violently at the world, searching for relief. And, more importantly, understanding. Eventually I learned to stop fighting and start living again.

Along the way, I discovered the secret to making friends with my pain.

As much as our society today talks about sharing feelings and "getting in touch" with ourselves, we are surprisingly inept at dealing with pain. We do not develop the skills needed to cope with it. Pain is not something we think about unless we are forced to. Until we are face-to-face with pain, we don't know what we will feel. How we will react. We do not have an action plan. We are completely unprepared.

I failed to realize this. I truly believed I could manage living with chronic illness. I had overcome many other obstacles in my life, so I didn't expect this experience to be any different. I felt I was strong enough. But I was wrong. This would be my most difficult challenge, and the one I was least prepared for.

Once I realized this, I reached out desperately for help. I was surprised to discover that expressions of personal physical pain are difficult for others to accept. Most people are uncomfortable to know that you are in pain. Unconsciously, they often ostracize those who suffer from it, because they fear something they cannot understand themselves.

I believe the root of the problem is that we tend to view pain as the enemy. We draw lines in the sand and prepare ourselves for battle. But expending energy in such a negative way serves no purpose. It is not the answer. It only causes you to feel worse. You must change your perception of pain. View it in a more positive and constructive way.

In order to live successfully with pain, you must build a relationship with it. Embrace it. Learn to give and to take. Negotiate. Compromise. You need to develop a friendship with your pain, just as you would with a person. Acknowledge and accept it. Once you establish a relationship, you must nurture it. Only when you begin to treat pain as *friend* rather than *foe* can you learn to live with it.

It's important, however, to be realistic. Change doesn't happen overnight. Be patient with your body and don't expect too much from it. You must believe things *can* get better. Set clear goals. Prepare yourself not for battle, but for a journey. The journey will be long, and once you have begun there's no turning back.

Along the way, you will discover a sense of peace. And it will all have been worth it.

I know my own journey will never end. There will always be goals to reach. Sometimes, there will even be setbacks. But my desire to continue will never falter. Not now, because I have come so far. I've learned from this experience that I *can* live with pain. Before, it was merely a hope. Now it is a reality.

I firmly believe in the saying "That which does not kill us makes us stronger." It is during the periods of adversity in my life that I have undergone the most significant personal growth. Facing my challenges rather than hiding from them has made me stronger, and, hopefully a better person. So it has been with this experience. As you read this book, you might find some of my suggestions impractical. You may think, "Sure, that's easy for her to say. Her life is much different than mine." That is irrelevant. It doesn't matter if you live alone or with a spouse and five children; if you work on Wall Street or run a small business out of your home. In order to be the best person you can be, for your loved ones *and* for yourself, you must learn to live well with your illness. Don't think of it as an option.

You *must* take care of your ailing body and build a relationship with your pain. Having other responsibilities does complicate things. But you can work around it. All it takes is desire. A desire to do the things that will make you feel well. There *is* time in your schedule; you just have to find it, as I did. You will soon discover that your priorities change.

Managing chronic illness requires great discipline. It's not an easy task. You can never slack off. Not for a second. It can be exhausting. But it's a journey you must commit yourself to. The alternative is to remain in great pain, keeping you from the life you were meant to live. You can't afford to give that up easily.

It is as a friend wrote so eloquently to me: "Pain is the bridge between illness and recovery. Some of us reach the other side quickly, others take a lifetime to cross. But you can't stand still enjoying the view, because everything might collapse beneath you. You must push on, across the bridge, one step at a time." You must commit yourself to the journey.

I wrote this book for people who live with chronic illness, their families and friends. I understand that not everything I suggest will apply to your personal situation. Your journey to wellness is your own; however, you won't know unless you give it a chance. Isn't it worth trying, if living well could be the result? I believe it is. We all deserve to live well. Some of us just have to climb a few more mountains along the way.

The most important thing to remember is that each person's experience with pain is unique. There is no universal experience. I can't tell you what will be most effective for you. No one can, including your doctors. The only way to discover your own path to living well is, unfortunately, through trial and error. You have to *feel* your way through. I only hope that revealing my personal successes and failures will enable you to take the first step. My wish for you is a good and successful journey!

# ~ CONTENTS ~

# DISCOVERY

When my own journey began, I had no idea it would change my life so completely. The symptoms seemed so inconsequential at the time. I was in good physical condition. I exercised regularly, ate well, maintained a weight I was happy with. My blood pressure was absolutely perfect. My cholesterol was low. I didn't smoke, and was only a social drinker. I was by all accounts a healthy twenty-nine year-old woman.

Sure, I'd had my ailments. My friends used to tease me about my eccentric maladies: shingles, migraine headaches, irritable bowel syndrome, and a painful, mysterious stomach condition that lasted eight months. But none of it was ever serious, or chronic. I wasn't the least bit prepared for what I was about to face.

It began in late summer. I noticed a strange tingling sensation in my feet while exercising. My first thought was that my shoes could be causing the problem. So I bought new ones. But the tingling continued. Rather than numbness, it was more like pins and needles, similar to what you feel when your foot falls asleep. It happened in both feet, up to the ankle. I told myself it was caused by poor circulation. Nothing to worry about.

Then it began to occur at other times. It was especially bad when I'd sit for long periods. I noticed it when I was canoeing with friends one weekend. It often happened at work as I sat at my desk. I mentioned it to a friend, and he said, "That's weird. You should call your doctor." That was in August.

But I didn't call my doctor. I did not feel I had cause to. I didn't want her to think I was paranoid, some kind of hypochondriac. I tried not to sit so much, and worked out for shorter periods of time, since the tingling would usually begin after twenty minutes or so of any one

activity. I varied my routines. Assumed the problem would just go away. Instead, it got worse.

Soon I was experiencing tingling in my
calves as well as my feet, all the way up to my
knees. It was happening more often, almost all
the time, in fact. It was noticeably worse when
working out, and I still assumed it was caused by
poor circulation. But when it spread to my
thighs in October, I made an appointment to
see my doctor.

First, my doctor ordered a test for
Diabetes. A nurse came into the room, pricked
my finger, and put a drop of blood into a tiny
machine which read my blood sugar. She asked
when I had eaten last, and said I was normal.
That was the first of many illnesses I'd be told I
*didn't* have.

The doctor returned and asked many
questions about my symptoms. It was like an
inquisition. To make matters worse, she had a
pharmaceutical representative following her
around that day, and she kept talking to him in
medical terms I didn't understand. It felt as
though they were discussing me in a foreign language, while I was in the room. I asked her what

she thought might be causing my symptoms. She said it could be lead poisoning, thyroid disease or a vitamin deficiency. To be safe, she would also check for evidence of cancer. Another nurse came in and drew blood to send to the lab.

About a week later, my doctor called. She said the test results were all normal. She asked if my symptoms were persisting. I said they were. The tingling was occurring more often, sometimes all day long, no matter what my activity. It was becoming extremely difficult to sustain any one position, whether sitting or standing, for any length of time. I was very uncomfortable. The only position I could bear to be in was lying down. She asked me to come back to her office.

On my next visit, I was put through a new series of tests. I was asked to walk toe to heel in a straight line. I had to hop on one foot. The doctor pricked me with needles to see if I could feel anything. She asked if I could tell the difference between sharp and soft objects against my skin. She checked my reflexes. She had me lie down on the table, and manipulated my legs around and around. She tested my arm and leg strength by having me push against her hand as hard as I could.

Of course, she asked more questions about my symptoms. When were they worse, or better? How did they start? Did they ever change? If so, what was I doing when they changed? Did I feel weak? X-rays of my spine were ordered, to look for any possible disc problems. They revealed nothing out of the ordinary.

My doctor told me she felt the problem was neurological, perhaps something called Guillain-Barré syndrome, an acute condition affecting the nervous system. It usually begins in the arms or legs, then spreads to the rest of the body. It can be serious, but is easy to treat if discovered early. She referred me to a neurologist, and forwarded all of her preliminary findings to his office.

It took a few weeks to schedule an appointment with the neurologist. When I did finally see him, there were more questions. Many of them were hard to answer, because it was extremely difficult to describe what I felt. There were times it was like pins and needles, and others when it felt more like tingling and numbness. Sometimes there was a burning sensation. But at that point, there was no pain.

The neurologist made me walk toe to heel again. Jump on one foot. Close my eyes, stick out my arms and stand still. Skip across the room. Bend over and touch the floor. Follow his finger with my eyes without moving my head. He asked me to look at a red piece of plastic, first with one eye, then the other. The color changed each time I switched eyes. From one eye, it looked like a light, yellowish red. From the other, I saw a deep, brownish red. He told me it was a sign that the problem was indeed neurological.

He felt there was definitely something going on. He just didn't know what. He ordered blood drawn, to look for evidence of demyelination, the breaking down of the myelin sheath that surrounds each nerve fiber. I asked him what the possibilities were. He didn't want to speculate, because it was too early in the evaluation process. So I went home, knowing nothing more than when I had left.

I received a call about a week later. The

neurologist told me all the tests were normal. I was relieved. But I wanted to know what he thought the next step should be. He told me it would be best to take a "wait and watch" approach, to see if my symptoms changed in any way. He suggested I keep a journal to record my symptoms on a daily basis, and come back to see him in a few weeks.

I wasn't particularly happy with that advice, but I took it. Who was I to question a specialist? Besides, while my symptoms were highly aggravating, they were not painful, nor did they disrupt most of my daily routines. I was able to work and continue my other activities. I was concerned, but not seriously so. So I took his advice, and made an appointment for a few weeks later.

Not long after that, the tingling/prickly sensations were occurring all the time. I was constantly getting up to walk around. That would bring temporary relief, but once I sat down again, or if I stood for too long, the symptoms would return. I was uncomfortable almost all the time, and it was growing increasingly difficult to find relief.

I was also experiencing extreme fatigue. I didn't have the energy to do anything. I came home at the end of the day absolutely drained. Sometimes, I'd go straight to bed. On the weekends, I slept almost constantly. It was difficult to get out of bed. I didn't have the strength.

I gave up trying to exercise. I'd begun to feel stiff in the muscles of my legs. I would stretch and stretch, but the stiffness wouldn't go away. It was like the feeling you have after overexerting yourself. You wake up the next morning, or on the second day, and are stiff and sore all over. That was how I felt all day long.

Walking up the three flights of stairs to my apartment became a serious challenge. I experienced weakness and fatigue in the muscles of my legs, especially the thighs. I could go up two flights without much trouble, but the third was tough. However, I still didn't consider my symptoms to be serious. Only irritating.

When I went back to the neurologist a few weeks later, I told him about my new symptoms. He asked more questions. The symptoms were still isolated to my legs and feet. I didn't have problems anywhere else. My legs, however, had gotten much worse. When I walked up stairs or hills, my legs felt like they would collapse. The muscles were tied up in knots.

He asked me how much of the time I was aware of my symptoms, and I said ninety percent. The only time I wasn't aware of them was when I slept, if I could sleep. That had become a real problem. I had trouble getting to sleep, because I was bothered by my symptoms. I woke up often during the night, uncomfortable. I remember tossing and turning for hours, and getting up in the morning exhausted.

At that point, the neurologist decided to order a Magnetic Resonance Imaging (MRI), to get a better look at my lower and upper spine and brain. As I understood it, radio waves would bounce off my body, forming clear images of my internal organs and tissues. Again I asked what he was looking for, and again he refused to answer. I began to worry.

I went to the hospital for an MRI. It was a very intimidating experience. A friend of mine has described it as "the closest I've ever been to being abducted by aliens." After changing into a set of scrubs, I was escorted into a large room.

The equipment took up almost the entire area. It was huge, and looked like something out of a science fiction movie. I had never felt so small in my life. Off to the side there was another room, which looked into the machine room through a large glass window.

The technician explained what was going to happen. I was to lie down on the table, and it would be pushed into the machine. It looked like a large tube. The testing would take a couple of hours, I was told, and it was important that I remain perfectly still. I was given earplugs for the first phase of the testing, which was to look at my upper and lower spine. The technician suggested I relax and try to sleep.

He must have thought he was being funny, because it sounded like a jackhammer was being used inside that capsule. There was no way anyone could sleep. The noises were deafening *with* earplugs! There were also very strong vibrations, and a variety of different sounds which followed a pattern.

I had a strange reaction to these noises. It was similar to being at a sporting event; when everyone starts clapping, you can't help but do it yourself. By the end of the test, I was humming all the different patterns of sounds in my head, and anticipating when they would change. I didn't want to; it was an involuntary reaction. But it was also a way to distract myself, because I was very much afraid.

Much to my dismay, my legs began to tingle only a few minutes into the test. It was agonizing trying to keep still, especially when I knew that moving would help. I did squirm a little bit, thinking they would probably yell at me. But they didn't. Luckily, I was brought out of the capsule after awhile and allowed to walk around. Then the second phase of testing began.

The technician placed a large restraining contraption on my head, resembling a plastic crate, and strapped me in. It insured that I could not move my head at all during the testing. This time, I was given headphones, and asked which radio station I would like to listen to. The second test was much shorter. After only a few minutes, I was pulled back out of the capsule, and a purple liquid was injected into my arm. It burned. The technician said it would help them see my brain better, and that it was a harmless substance. Back into the capsule I went.

I was at the hospital for more than three hours. It was dark when I left, and snowing. I remember well. I wished I had taken my parents up on their offer to go with me. I had never felt so completely alone. Now, I had to wait for the results. My neurologist had told me it could be as long as a week. He promised he would call as soon as he received the written report from the hospital.

When you don't know what is happening to your body, one day feels like a week. You are scared. It was torment having to wait for that phone call. I was conjuring up many worst-case scenarios in my head. When I hadn't heard anything after a week, I telephoned my neurologist's office to check on the results. That night, he called me at home.

"Good news," he said, "Everything looks normal." I was relieved, but also a bit disappointed, because I was still no closer to an answer. Slowly but surely, we were eliminating different possibilities. But where did that leave me? Once again I asked him what the next step would be. He suggested we continue to wait and watch.

I completely lost it. At that point, I'd been experiencing symptoms for almost four months. Wait and see? I didn't want to wait any longer. I wanted answers. I wanted to know what was going on with my body. I told him I was not happy with his advice, that I was tired of taking a "wait and see" approach. I'm sure he could hear my exasperation, I was almost yelling. In retrospect, I was embarrassed by my reaction; my emotions had taken over.

He cautioned me not to be too eager to move forward. The next possible tests, he said, would be painful. He told me he could order a lumbar puncture, or spinal tap, but there were risks. The procedure involves inserting a long needle into the spinal canal to obtain a sample of fluid. Besides being painful, he told me that many women of child-bearing age experience a post-spinal tap headache, which is worse than a migraine and can last up to a week.

There was also something called a nerve conduction study, but it was extremely painful.

It uses electric pulses to test for nerve damage. He preferred waiting, to see if my symptoms changed in any way, giving him some idea of what action to take next. He told me to come back to his office in a month, unless there were any noticeable changes before then.

It made sense, but who cares about sense when you are sick? Still, I had no choice but to wait. I could have gone to another doctor, I suppose, but I couldn't bear the thought of starting over again with all those questions. Besides, my team of doctors had not yet exhausted every possible resource. Changing doctors could actually lengthen the time it took to get to an answer. So I waited.

I think the main problem I had with the neurologist was his approach. He was very abrupt, and I wasn't used to that. It seemed that we had trouble communicating. He suspected as much, and contacted my primary care physician, who then called me to talk about it. She wanted to know if I had any problems working with the neurologist. She reiterated her confidence in him, but said if I wasn't comfortable, we could try someone else.

I was impressed that both of them were concerned about the matter. I was particularly touched that my doctor would call to reassure me I was getting the best possible care. I told her I was comfortable working with the neurologist; I was just frustrated by the process we had to go through to get to the bottom of things. She understood, and said that if I had any questions or problems at all, I should call her.

I prayed my symptoms would change, so the doctors could reach a diagnosis. I assumed that whatever was wrong could be fixed quickly and easily. Has anyone ever told you, "Be careful what you wish for, because you just might get it?" My symptoms changed just a few days later, on November 25th, as I was heading back to work from my lunch hour.

Walking up a small hill through the parking lot, I began to feel very strange. It's extremely difficult to put into words. If you have ever been given a general anesthetic before surgery, you might understand, because that's what it felt like. All of a sudden, it was as if I were no longer in my body. I felt light-headed, detached from myself. It was almost like being in a state of semi-consciousness.

My legs felt as if they were made of lead. With every step, I feared they would collapse under my weight. I managed to walk up the stairs and into the lobby. I told the receptionist I felt "a little weird." I heard myself saying the words, but it was as if I were outside of myself looking in, floating above my body.

When I got to my desk, things started to go black. I sat down and put my head in my hands. I was very dizzy. My vision was blurred and everything was moving rapidly in front of my face. I could not focus on anything. The radio sounded like it was miles away. I couldn't speak without slurring my words. My legs were trembling. And then I could no longer feel my body. I wasn't conscious of any sensation at all. It was terrifying.

After about ten minutes, the "attack" (for lack of a better word), appeared to be over. As soon as I was able, I dialed the neurologist's number, and told him what was going on. He said I should wait by the phone. He was going to call my internist and consult with her. The next phone call that came was from her office.

"Go to the Emergency Room immediately," she said. "I will let them know you are coming."

I had to call my parents to come and pick me up, because I was afraid to drive. It was quiet in the ER that evening, so I was seen right away. There were more questions, which I was sick of by now, and which grew harder and harder to answer. I tried to explain all the tests I'd already been through. The physician at the ER called my doctor to speak to her about my case.

When he came back, he said the only thing left to do was an Electro Cardiogram (EKG) to check my heart. It's a simple procedure. Electric impulses in the heart are recorded on a strip of paper. Small metal "contacts" were taped to the skin of my arms, legs and chest to measure the flow and direction of electric currents in my heart. Just the thought that they would do that for a woman my age was alarming. But they assured me when it was over that everything looked fine.

The doctor did mention that I had a heart murmur. It was the first time anyone had told me that. I was concerned about it, knowing nothing about such a condition. I thought any

problem with the heart was potentially danger-
ous. But no one in the Emergency Room
seemed alarmed by it. The doctor told me it
was not serious.

The physician in charge of the ER came
in and talked to me for awhile, asked more questions. She explained that I had experienced a
"near syncope episode," which basically means
I had almost fainted. She said that in 90% of
fainting episodes, no definitive cause is ever
found. Because they didn't feel I was in any
immediate danger, I was discharged, and told to
follow up with my doctor the next day.

By this time, I was growing increasingly
frightened. The near-fainting experience had
unnerved me. I went to my doctor's office and
pleaded with her to tell me what she thought
was going on. She said that she and the neurologist suspected I might have Multiple Sclerosis.
At least, that was the most logical possibility at
that time. But my symptoms were not following
the pattern of any one condition. My doctors
were quite perplexed. She told me not to get too
worried. It may not be MS, but it was a possibility they had to explore.

I asked her about the heart murmur. She listened and told me there was indeed a slight murmur. She said it sounded like it was a "flow murmur" and was nothing to be concerned about. I mentioned that I had experienced palpitations, an unusually high heart rate. She told me it was probably caused by the stress of the situation.

By now, I was hypersensitive to any perceived changes in my body. I wanted so desperately to find an answer, that when the doctors gave me a possible cause, I began to look for evidence. I would read up on a condition and think, "I could have this." I didn't care what was wrong at that stage. I just wanted to *know*.

I went home and began an Internet search for information about Multiple Sclerosis (MS). I didn't like what I read. It is a degenerative disease, progressing through the years. Many patients end up in a wheelchairs, unable to walk. Some go blind. I hoped against all hope that I did not have MS.

I already had another appointment scheduled with the neurologist. When I went, he explained that there were several more blood tests he would like to conduct. He wanted to screen for HIV & AIDS, Rheumatoid Arthritis, Lupus and Lyme disease. He also ordered a nerve conduction study, which measures the nervous system's ability to send messages to the brain.

In some countries, electrocution is used as a means of torture. In the United States, electrocution is the method by which many convicted criminals have been executed. Doctors use it in the name of science. It was without a doubt the worst pain I'd ever experienced in my life. It made any other discomfort seem like a pin prick or a mosquito bite.

I donned yet another flimsy hospital gown, and was told to lie on a cold table. Tiny wires were taped to my skin, and electrical currents were sent through my body. They started out weak, then grew stronger and stronger. My body twitched uncontrollably, and just when I'd think I couldn't take any more, they would stop. The wires would be moved to a different area of my body, and the process would be repeated.

I have no idea how long I was on that table. I just kept praying it would end soon, so the doctor wouldn't see me cry. I had to bite my tongue to keep from yelling out. He probably wouldn't have noticed, because he was staring at the computer which read my nervous system's reaction to each wave of electric current and charted it on a graph. A printout revealed that my reactions were normal. There was no neuropathy, or damage to the nerves. One more possibility ruled out. It was back to square one.

The blood test results were not expected for several more days. So I did my best to continue with life as usual. But I was unable to distract myself. I couldn't stop thinking about what was wrong with me, and why it was so difficult to determine. What if they never found out? If the symptoms just went away one day, that would be fantastic. But what if they went on and on with no resolution? How would I cope? I was becoming despondent. Then it happened.

I will never forget the day the pain began. It was in December. I was at work. (I am Creative Services Coordinator for a privately held St. Louis company.) I was standing in a warehouse, gathering products for a photo shoot. Suddenly there was a severe, searing pain in my hips and thighs. It took my breath away. It was a pain deep inside my muscles. A throbbing, stabbing pain. I had never experienced anything like it. I told the person I was with I had to leave.

I got into my car and called the neurologist. I told him I was in terrible pain, and asked if there was something he could give me for it. He told me he had just received my test results from the lab. No HIV, AIDS, Arthritis or Lyme disease, but my anti-nuclear antibody (ANA) count was above normal, which indicated I might have Lupus.

Once again, he was going to call my internist. And once again, she called me back. She told me the next step would be to see a rheumatologist, a doctor who specializes in Arthritis and other related conditions. She gave me a name and number, and said she would call the office and speak with the rheumatologist before I went in. To lessen my discomfort, she prescribed Naproxen, an anti-inflammatory drug.

It had no effect at all on my pain. The next day, my mother and I hosted a bridal shower for my best friend. It was difficult to get through it and not let the pain show. I had difficulty walking. Sitting was excruciating. Just breathing normally was a challenge. I couldn't imagine having to live like that all the time.

The friend we were having the shower for happens to have Lupus, an autoimmune disease which causes inflammation of the joints, tendons, muscles and sometimes organs. The body basically begins to attack itself. It can be fatal, but is usually just debilitating. I thought, if this is what it's like, I don't want any part of it. I wondered how my friend managed it. My admiration for her grew ten times that day.

The rheumatologist was a very gentle woman. I liked her immediately. She asked considerably more detailed questions and performed a thorough physical examination. She wanted to know everything about my medical history. She told me she didn't think my condition was Lupus. My symptoms didn't fit the pattern, but some were suspicious, so she would have to conduct more tests. First she took a urine sample to check for kidney damage (Lupus sometimes affects the kidneys). Then she ordered blood tests.

I went to the lab, where six tubes of blood were taken from my arm. They were testing for a wide variety of antibodies in my blood, and other indicators of Lupus. I had no idea what that meant; I just asked when the results would be in. It was the week of Christmas, so the nurse said it could take as long as two weeks.

The only thing I remember about that Christmas is being in severe pain. It was overwhelming. And there was no escaping it. Again, it was as if I were not inside my body. Like I was watching it happen to someone else. It wasn't me. It couldn't be. The experience just didn't seem real. I tried desperately to maintain some sense of a 'normal' life. I went to holiday parties, sporting events, anything to keep my mind off the pain. It was all in vain.

The pain began to play with my mind. I had a hard time concentrating, and it was difficult to carry on a conversation. I also had trouble remembering things. I prayed constantly for God to take the pain away. All I really wanted was to fall asleep and never wake up. The pain was unrelenting.

I discovered that heat offered temporary relief, so I spent much of the time in bed with a heating pad. Or on the floor in my living room. I took frequent hot baths, which also offered a temporary escape from the pain. I initially continued to take the medication my doctor had prescribed, but it did absolutely no good. Actually, there were some unpleasant side effects, so I eventually stopped taking it.

It was during this period that my problems with sleeping worsened. I had difficulty falling asleep, because the pain was so great. It would take hours of tossing and turning before I could sleep. I would then wake up as many as five times a night. I'd have to get up, walk around and try stretching.

That would produce a strange sensation. It hurt to stretch, but it also felt good in a strange kind of way. But no amount of stretching could decrease the pain or stiffness. Sometimes I would try the heating pad, which was now my constant companion. Or I would simply get into bed and turn the electric blanket on "high."

I had one heating pad at home, and one at work. Sitting was extremely uncomfortable.

In fact, there was no position that was comfortable. I was in agony all the time. I walked around the office constantly. I went home and lay on the floor in front of the TV with the heating pad. There was no relief. The pain never let up. I was now aware of it 24 hours a day.

The stiffness and pain were also on the move. I began to feel extreme discomfort in my neck, shoulders and arms. The throbbing pain would occur in my upper arms, forearms and hands. I would massage my shoulders and neck until my strength gave out. But the stiffness would never go away.

I had strong, stabbing pains in the muscles of my chest. (This really scared me until I later learned from my physical therapist that it was common in FMS patients.) The only areas that were not affected at the time were my abdominal and back muscles. That would change soon enough.

The answer to why Naproxen hadn't worked came the week after New Year's Day. I didn't have Lupus. There was no inflammation. So, naturally, an anti-inflammatory would not work. But what would? The rheumatologist *sug-*

*gested I had injured myself on the Stairmaster.* She prescribed a new medicine, Flexeril, which is a muscle relaxant. I could take it at night before going to bed. She said the "injury" would probably just clear up one day.

Then she dismissed me. Told me to go back to my regular doctor. I knew in my heart that my pain was not caused by an injury. It had gone on too long, spread too far. I was frustrated that she would attempt to dismiss my symptoms so callously. But what could I do? Scream at her? Demand a second opinion? What purpose would that serve? It would get me no closer to an answer.

When the breakthrough finally came, it was from an unexpected source. A friend of the family told my mom about something called Fibromyalgia Syndrome (FMS). Her daughter had been having health problems, and had been diagnosed with FMS and Chronic Fatigue Immune Deficiency Syndrome (CFIDS), two closely related disorders. When my mom told her about my symptoms, she said it sounded hauntingly familiar.

I called her one night to talk about it. It

sounded like her daughter's primary problem was fatigue. For me, fatigue was secondary to the pain. But I did have some of the same symptoms as her daughter. She was able to tell me details about the illness, and even suggested some books I could look for. Most importantly, I learned from her what questions I needed to ask my doctors next.

I went to see my internist again. We talked about all my symptoms, and how they had progressed. I asked her if she knew about FMS, and she said it was indeed a possibility. But a diagnosis can't be made until all other possibilities have been ruled out. There is, unfortunately, no diagnostic test for FMS. As a general rule of thumb, a diagnosis is not considered until a patient has experienced widespread pain for at least three months.

I told her Flexeril had been helping with the pain at night. She wrote a new prescription and increased my dosage. She also prescribed a mild anti-depressant called Elavil. Not because I was depressed, but because it often helps with sleeping. I asked her if there were any exercises that would be safe for me to do. I was used to being very active, and was growing frustrated with my inability to exercise. She decided it was time for me to see a physical therapist, and gave me a referral.

My first appointment was in mid-January. The physical therapist asked all about my symptoms. He put me through a number of physical tests. I told him that my doctor said I might have Fibromyalgia. He asked if I thought I did. I said I really didn't know. When the doctors thought it was Multiple Sclerosis, I thought they might be right. Same thing with Lupus. My symptoms fell into the descriptions of both diseases. But there were also symptoms I did not have. So I really didn't know what to think. I just wanted to feel better.

He said that because the majority of my symptoms involved my legs, and were worst when sitting, he would like to give me a few back and neck exercises to try. He said a simple thing like posture can sometimes be the cause of such problems. He showed me how I should sit at my desk at work; how to arrange my things. He demonstrated two exercises to help stretch the muscles in my back and neck. He said to do them four times a day and come back in a week.

I did the exercises religiously. They hurt a bit, but in a strange way they felt good, too. I paid extremely close attention to my posture. But there was no noticeable change in my symptoms. When I went back in a week, the physical therapist added a few more exercises. This went on for about a month. I saw him every week, and did my exercises every day. He kept adding more and more exercises, until I was working on all the major muscle groups. I was supposed to do each exercise several times a day.

By this time, there was a pattern emerging. I would be doing well for awhile, and then something would happen to cause a flare-up, resulting in terrible pain for a week or more. Sometimes I could identify what I had done to bring on the pain, but not always. Usually, it was from straining my muscles, or from repetitive action of some kind (bending over, squatting, carrying boxes, writing, typing...).

After watching this pattern continue for a few months, the physical therapist was convinced I did have Fibromyalgia. To confirm this, he applied manual pressure to several so-called "tender" or "trigger points" on my body. Patients with Fibromyalgia Syndrome experience an abnormal amount of pain when pressure is applied to these specific points on the body.

I definitely felt extreme pain when he touched me at some of those points. This confirmed his suspicion that it was FMS. In my case, he said, the initial goal would be to lengthen the amount of time between flare-ups. After that, we would focus on minimizing flare-ups when they did occur.

He showed me a variety of stretches I could do to increase my flexibility and to help with the stiffness. These were in addition to the exercises I had already been doing. I was supposed to stretch several times a day. I asked about exercise. He said not yet. He told me to be patient, that I would be able to get my body back in shape someday. But it would take time.

In February I went back to my doctor's office. We talked about the medication I was taking. I had noticed some improvement in getting to sleep, but I was not sleeping through the night. There were also a number of side effects from the drugs I was taking. One of the medications caused me to have a dry mouth all the time. I also had daytime drowsiness, but it was hard to tell if that was caused by my medicine or the fatigue from FMS itself.

The diagnosis of Fibromyalgia Syndrome finally came in late February, seven months after the onset of my symptoms. It had been a very difficult time. And even though I still felt awful, I was relieved to at last have a name for my pain. To know I was not crazy. There *was* a reason for the pain I was experiencing. But the journey was far from over. Now I had to learn how to manage my condition, which would take great discipline. More than I could possibly imagine.

Fibromyalgia Syndrome (FMS) was not widely recognized until the early 1990's. It is a connective tissue disorder - "fibro"referring to the muscles, tendons and ligaments of the body, and "myalgia" meaning pain. The primary symptoms are widespread pain, stiffness, numbing, tingling, fatigue and sleep disorders.

The symptoms of FMS can be affected by weather, lack of exercise, overexertion, hormonal levels, activity, stress, time of day, or by no noticeable factor at all. It can affect different areas of the body. Many patients hurt all over. My own pain is usually worst in the muscles of my legs, particularly the thighs. But I do feel it in different areas at different times (e.g. the neck, shoulders, chest, back, arms and hands).

Fatigue and sleep disturbances are as much of a problem as pain. FMS patients are often light or restless sleepers who wake easily and frequently during the night. In the deepest stages of sleep, our bodies renew, regenerate and repair themselves. In FMS patients, deep sleep is often interrupted. So when a patient wakes, he or she does not feel rested. This is definitely true of me. When I do not get deep, restorative sleep, my fatigue and pain during the day are worse.

Most medication taken by FMS patients focuses on improving sleep quality. Once patients are able to get deep, restorative sleep, they notice that their symptoms are diminished. Sleep is, therefore, vital to the successful management of Fibromyalgia. Not getting enough quality sleep can make symptoms worse.

Secondary symptoms of FMS can include irritable bowel syndrome, migraine headaches, memory and concentration problems and restless leg syndrome. I have experienced several of these. In fact, I had many of these problems long before I developed FMS. I was diagnosed with irritable bowel syndrome (IBS) over five years go. Three years ago, I began to suffer from migraine headaches. Now I wonder if they were related, early signs of the disorder.

The good news about Fibromyalgia is that there is a great deal of information available today on the disorder. The medical community has recently begun to take a close look at FMS, and diagnosis and treatment have come a long way in the past few years. We now know much more than we did just five years ago. Hopefully, researchers will find a cure in the near future.

While this has been a very difficult experience for me, I consider myself to be extremely fortunate. I've heard of many people who suffered from pain for years without receiving a diagnosis. They were told it was all in their heads and referred to psychiatrists. Because doctors did not recognize FMS, patients who suffered from the disorder did not receive proper treatment. My experience sounds like nothing compared to their nightmares.

A friend of mine was sick and in pain for *seven years* before she found a doctor who would take her seriously. Once they began to look for a cause, she underwent three more years of testing before a diagnosis was made. She, and the other patients I speak of, have my deepest respect.

It is difficult to estimate how many people lived with FMS before there was a name for the disorder. As a result of their suffering, we know more about Fibromyalgia and how to manage it successfully. It's unfortunate that they were unable to benefit from these discoveries. I was desperate for results after only a few months of pain. Some patients had to live with pain their entire lives with no answers. I can only imagine how awful that must have been.

I have been blessed with a brilliant primary care physician and an exceptionally competent physical therapist. They never doubted that my pain was real. They did not give up until they found answers. Never once did they imply my symptoms were all in my head. We worked together as a team. We accomplished our goal. We reached a diagnosis. Our continued teamwork would be vital in my quest to live well with Fibromyalgia.

# FIGHT OR FLIGHT

**W**hen a person is diagnosed with a chronic illness, he or she goes through a grieving period. Grieving is loss. The diagnosis of a chronic condition is perceived as a kind of loss, and rightfully so. You grieve for the things in your life that are lost forever. You grieve because you realize that nothing is ever going to be the same.

Life as you know it has been forever changed. Your relationships will be affected. Your work will be affected. Your social life will be affected. Obviously, your health is affected. Every aspect of your life will be different in some way as a result of your illness. Allow yourself time to grieve. It is a natural and necessary part of the healing process. Don't let anyone tell you differently. In fact, *not* grieving can be detrimental to your physical and mental well-being.

The initial reaction to the diagnosis of a chronic condition is often shock. Disbelief. This is a normal response to such life-altering news. In today's world, where medical technology is thought to be omnipotent, we expect easy solutions. Science has advanced a great deal. Surely the doctors can fix it, you think to yourself. Why can't they just give you some pills to make it go away?

That is what I was looking for. Throughout the long testing period, when my doctors were trying to figure out what was going on, I assumed the solution would be simple. Why wouldn't it be? I knew early on we were not dealing with something life-threatening. So why wouldn't the answer be simple?

Much of this confidence in the medical profession can be traced to the entertainment industry. How many sick people have you seen on TV, or in the movies? Not many. Illness was a subject most studios did not want to touch until recently. It was too realistic. Too depressing. It might affect ratings negatively. In the rare case that a character did become ill, the treatment and recovery were rarely portrayed realistically.

It always seemed as if the person miraculously got well. It was uncommon to see a character suffer. And it was the exception, not the rule, when a diagnosis actually came to fruition. How often was a character told he has a few months to live, only to suddenly recover and appear on the show for another year?

As I said, this has been changing in recent years. The unfortunate legacy, however, is that we have a false sense of security about doctors and medicine. The examples that are set for us are not true to life. Even now, the media tends to focus on people who are dying, not those who *live* with their illnesses.

We don't want to believe that health professionals can't fix us. It would destroy us. We need to have hope. A light at the end of the tunnel. It's much easier to suspend what we know to be true and replace it with a fantasy. It is our attempt to escape, if only temporarily.

Escape is indeed your first desire. As the

impact of your situation starts to hit home, shock and disbelief slowly turn to denial. It is difficult to accept that you will be sick for *the rest of your life*. Those words seem so final. And you have yet to fully comprehend what they mean.

I wanted my doctor to write a prescription, give me a shot, do anything that would make my pain go away. Finding out that nothing could was a real blow. Accepting that I would suffer from Fibromyalgia Syndrome for the rest of my life was almost more than I could bear. I did not want to believe it was true. I couldn't.

So I denied the facts. Rejected the reality of my situation. We all do this. It is the mind's way of protecting itself. We think if we ignore the pain, it will go away. If we refuse to accept that we are sick, then we won't really be sick. If we pretend nothing is different in our lives, then maybe nothing will be. We continue with our regular routines, refusing to change in any way. We expend great energy in our attempts to deny pain.

Denial is an essential step in the grieving process. It is, in fact, helpful - *for a time*. Denial gives your body a chance to build up the resources it needs to deal with the pain. The initial shock is too much for your mind to handle, so it shuts down until it is ready to face the facts. Denial gives your body time to prepare, to establish a plan of attack. You need to shore up your reserves. Remember, your body believes it is gearing up for battle.

In the beginning, it is easy to deny pain. The only other option, acceptance, is unpleasant at best. And you are not yet ready to face your illness. Besides, the people around you are also in denial. My dad was one of those people. He did not want to face the fact that I was sick, and would be for life.

He kept telling me it would go away. Just as denial was part of my grieving process, it was for him a coping mechanism. I know he didn't mean to hurt me. He just wasn't ready to accept the diagnosis. But it did hurt. I felt like he was belittling my pain.

I knew my dad was worried about me, and didn't quite know how to handle the situation. Still, I got upset with him. One night we had a heated exchange. I was sharing with my parents some of the things my physical therapist told me about FMS. My dad began to argue with me about whether I was really sick:

"You don't have Fibromyalgia," he said.

"Yes I do," I answered.

"How do you know that?"

"I've been diagnosed with it."

"Your physical therapist can't make that diagnosis. He doesn't know anything about Fibromyalgia."

"Yes, he does. He knows a lot about it. That's his job."

"He's not a doctor. Only a doctor can make a diagnosis. He doesn't know what he is talking about."

"Yes, he does. And my doctor has made that diagnosis."

"She has?"

"Yes."

"She said you have Fibromyalgia?"

"Yes."

"She said positively, or just maybe?"

"Positively."

"Your doctor told you that you do?"

"Yes."

"When did she say that?"

"At my last appointment."

"She said you have Fibromyalgia?"

"Yes. I have Fibromyalgia."

"But it will go away someday."

"No.  It won't."

"How do you know it won't go away?"

"Because it is a chronic condition."

"But there is a chance it might just go away."

"No, there isn't."

"If you have a negative attitude, you won't ever get better."

"I'm being realistic, not negative.  I'm going to have to manage FMS for the rest of my life."

"Well, no one told me that you definitely have Fibromyalgia.  I thought it was just a possibility."

"No.  That is the diagnosis."

"Oh."

At that point, he left the dinner table. I was furious with him. I wanted to scream, but that wasn't going to help anything. My mom knew how upset I was, and tried to change the subject. I had talked to her about my frustration with my parents. But I never had a chance to talk to my dad about my illness the way I did with her. We hadn't had the opportunity. Even though I love him dearly, I began to resent him. Now I understand *why* he acted the way he did.

Patients are not the only ones who experience denial. Your family and friends know as well as you do that this is going to change your life forever, and theirs. That is hard for them to face. It is difficult to accept, because they have no choice in the matter. Of course, neither do you. So, in a sense they do understand what you are going through, but in a different way.

To be honest, they are too concerned about how your illness will affect *them* to offer much support. They don't know what to do. They become uncomfortable with you, and you with them. It's much easier for all involved to deny the facts. Put aside the emotions. Continue living a "normal" life. But eventually, you have to move on.

You have to understand that your illness is a permanent part of your life. You will probably come to this acceptance before your family and friends will. They will continue to struggle with the issue, as you begin to deal with other powerful emotions. Don't wait for them to catch up. *Focus on yourself.* Continue to work through *your* grieving process.

It won't be easy. Once I did come to the realization that the pain was here to stay, I became angry. The anger grew inside of me, getting stronger and stronger. I hated the pain, and despised it for invading my life. I believed the pain was in control, and became resentful. I was terrified, and expressed my fear as anger. I no longer denied the pain, but fought it. Vehemently.

The natural instinct is to fight. When you experience pain, your body immediately goes on the defensive. It feels vulnerable, and seeks an escape from the situation. When one is not readily available, it declares war. This is the "fight or flight" response; your body's way of protecting itself by sending messages to the brain that there is danger ahead. The only difference is that flee-ing is not an option for people suffering from chronic pain and illness. There is no real escape. So you fight. It's an instinctive, internal reaction.

Our society reinforces the idea that we should fight. We are bombarded daily with images which carry that message. Not fighting back is viewed as a sign of weakness. If you don't fight back, you deserve what you get. Cowards are not treated kindly by our society. So you are more than willing to move forward with your attack plan.

Advertising tells us to fight pain. Companies claim their products can "beat" pain. We are constantly exposed to slogans such as "Win the war against pain" and "Get tough on pain." The message is everywhere, though we may not always be aware of it. It's as if your reaction has already been decided for you.

You prepare yourself to stay and fight. React not unlike an animal cornered in a cage. You feel that way, too. Trapped against your will. On the defensive. It doesn't matter if you win or lose, as long as you go down fighting. You vow to fight until you have no energy left. After all, you have no choice. It's you or the pain, or at least that is what you may think at the time.

I fought my pain initially by refusing to accept it. I would not submit. I would not let it change my life. I had an "you can't get me" attitude. I hadn't yet learned what my pain needed to survive, so I withheld everything from it. I wanted it to die. I guess I thought I could starve it out. I'm not really sure. Rational thought was not coming into play at that point. I was merely reacting. Taking a defensive position. Going on the attack. Learning to hate.

Along with the hate, I began to resent my pain. I grew extremely bitter. Fibromyalgia got in the way of my being able to do things I wanted to do. Things everybody else could do. My pain set me apart. Any time I couldn't do something, I was labeled as different. At least that's what I thought, because I felt different. I was keenly aware of my new limitations, and assumed everyone else was as well. That was not the kind of attention I wanted.

I'll give you an example. On a weekend in late February, I went to the home of a friend who lives near the route of the annual Mardi

Gras parade. Each year he hosts a large party before, during and after the parade. I found that while everyone stood around talking, laughing and drinking on his patio, I was unable to participate fully. I could neither stand for a long time nor drink alcohol.

It was the first time I had encountered this type of situation since my diagnosis. I realized then that my social life had to change drastically. I was very uncomfortable. I felt as though I stood out, that I was different in a noticeable way. Several things people said contributed to that feeling. Many acted shocked that I would turn down an offer for beer.

I don't mean to imply that you can't have a good time without alcohol. But social drinking had often been part of my relationships. Getting together with friends meant having a beer or two. It is noticeable when I don't drink. As a matter of fact, many times that was how we found out when our friends were expecting a baby. If the wife wasn't drinking, someone would make a comment. Then the couple would share their news. But that was not my situation.

It was difficult to explain to people why I couldn't drink. At first, I'd tell them I was on medication. But they asked what kind of medication I was taking. I didn't want to tell them, because many people recognize the names of anti-depressant drugs. I was afraid I would be labeled a "head case," a person with mental problems.

Telling them I couldn't drink because of a health condition was no better. I tried to keep it general, but people always pressed for details. It was awkward, however, because even though they had asked, they didn't really want to know. If I began to explain, some people seemed to look horrified. They avoided making eye contact. People would suddenly pretend to be interested in a conversation across the room. Sometimes, the way others reacted made me feel like a freak.

But there was more to my frustration than that. I *wanted* to have a beer. I liked it. I also enjoyed an occasional glass of wine. I was angry that I could no longer do that. I was in a state of grieving for a "lifestyle" I could no longer have. That was the beginning of a long period of anger and frustration.

At that point, I had just recently been diagnosed and begun treatment. I could still only stand for short periods of time before I would have to find a place to sit down. The only way to do that was to go inside. That separated me physically from everyone else at the party. I was the only person in the room. At one point, a man came up to me and asked if I was bored. He assumed I was trying to get away from the party. Nothing could have been further from the truth.

Eventually, we all went out to watch the parade. We ended up standing on a sidewalk along the route. It didn't take long for the pain to come. It was the same searing pain I had experienced that first day in the warehouse. I tried to ignore it, but there was no way I could. It was unbearable. So bad, in fact, that I was unable to see straight. The scene around me was fuzzy. It felt as though I wasn't part of the crowd.

When I told my friends, they looked shocked. They didn't understand why I would leave before the parade was over. Most seemed unable to grasp the amount of pain I was in. I had to fight my way through the crowd to get to where I had parked my car. I wasn't sure if I would make it. I feared I would pass out from the pain.

I went home, got into bed, and turned my electric blanket on high. I was furious. I was thinking about all my friends, still partying and having a great time. I imagined they were talking about me. It wasn't fair. I hated the pain with every inch of my being. Blamed it for ruining my weekend. I even accused it of trying to destroy my life.

FMS also affected some aspects of my professional life. For example, several months after my diagnosis, and early in treatment, a call came from one of my company's divisions. They desperately needed help to fill a new customer's order. My supervisor volunteered our department. Normally, this would be no problem for me. I was always one of the first to step forward to help.

This particular circumstance, however, was most likely going to cause me pain. It involved standing in a warehouse (the same one where the pain began months before) and pulling items from shelves. There would be lifting, bending, and several other activities I had been told to avoid. But I didn't want to say "no." I didn't want to stand out among my colleagues. I was extremely self-conscious. It was such an awful feeling. I can't find words to describe it.

I remember thinking and thinking about it until just before the time we were supposed to leave. I was distressed. I wanted to go with everyone else, but I knew it would cause considerable pain. There was no question about that. But how would I tell people? And how would they react? Would they "label" me? Look at me differently? I agonized over this for an hour. I was so upset, I wanted to cry.

At that point, few people at work knew about my health problems. Some had heard things through the "rumor mill," but not many of my co-workers really knew what was wrong with me. As far as I was concerned, being one of the only people not to go to the other office would definitely make me stand out. I desperately wanted to keep that from happening. I didn't want people to question my ability to do my job, as some will do when they learn an employee is chronically ill.

In the end, I had no choice. I could not compromise my health. I couldn't take such a risk. Especially since I had been feeling better. It would set me back several weeks, erasing much of the progress I had made. I would be a fool to go. My boss asked me to tell one of our executive officers personally. He was making the list of people who would help.

I was apprehensive when I went to his office. There was another employee there, arranging carpools. I told them I could not go. They became concerned and asked why. I said it was for health reasons. Both stared at me with the kind of look usually reserved for the dying. I was self-conscious, and remained so for a long time. Even though they said they understood, I felt I was somehow inadequate.

That incident made many people I had not wanted to know aware of my situation. They were curious, of course, and asked many questions. I tried to downplay it. I didn't want people to make a big deal of my situation. Or make a fuss over me. Or label me as different.

Episodes like this caused me to remain in an angry state for a long time. I was very negative, assuming I was going to be miserable for the rest of my life. I feared nothing would ever get better. In fact, there was a possibility things could become even worse. The future was a complete unknown. My hopes and dreams seemed very much in jeopardy. So I kept fighting. It made the most sense at the time. I didn't know what else to do.

This may sound familiar to you. The result is always the same. The pain gets worse. It becomes so great, you are unable to function normally. Your body becomes exhausted by the constant struggle, and eventually gives out. Waves the white flag of surrender. You've harbored so much anger that it sends your body into meltdown. Depression sets in. The will to fight dies. You wonder how you will ever make it. How can you live with such pain all the time?

As your anger slowly dies, you become depressed. You constantly ask "Why?" Why did this have to happen to me? Why do I have to have so much pain? Why do I feel like I have no control over my body? Why doesn't anybody understand what I am going through? Why can't my life go back to the way it was before? So many questions… And very few answers.

I spent a great deal of time crying. Everything seemed so hopeless. As my anger melted, it exited my body in the form of tears. Lots of tears. In a way, it was very therapeutic. Alone, at home, I could let out the emotions I had spent all day trying to conceal. There was no one there to judge me. I could be angry and sad. I could feel sorry for myself. But there was also a part of it that wasn't helpful.

It got to the point where I only left my home to go to work. I took pleasure in nothing. I didn't want to be around people, and that was fine with them, because I wasn't much fun to be with. I was in mourning for a life I felt was gone. I wallowed in self-pity. When I did reach out to people, I sensed they were rejecting me.

There were other reasons to be depressed. The illness had changed more than just my life. It had altered my appearance. I may have seemed healthy to others, but I did not feel I looked well. I was bothered by the changes I witnessed in my appearance. I had huge, black circles under my eyes from fatigue. They rarely went away. My skin was pale, dry, scaly, and lacked radiance. The texture of my hair changed. I developed dandruff for the first time in my life.

I gained a considerable amount of weight. Some of it could be attributed to my medication. But there was no doubt that my sudden inactivity also had a negative effect. I was very aware of the differences. I felt as if I were walking around in a stranger's body. I wanted desperately to give it back.

I tried hard to lose weight. I didn't want to meet new people, because I was afraid they would judge me by my appearance. It got to the point where many of my clothes wouldn't fit. Although most said nothing, I could tell people noticed. This did not improve my state of mind. The worst part was that I was in great shape before Fibromyalgia affected my body.

The changes in my life were obvious. I could no longer ignore them. At the height of my depression, I realized I was going to have to face my illness. My condition was growing worse. The only way to change that was to accept my illness and learn to live with it.

I was ready. Even excited. Things had to get better. I anticipated positive changes. Visualized a better state of existence. That gave me the strength to move on. FMS didn't have to ruin my life. I could regain control if I was willing to learn. If I gave up the fight.

Denial. Anger. Depression. They are all normal steps in the grieving process. They are perfectly healthy. Do not despair. You must work through the *entire* process before you can move forward. Sooner or later you will reach acceptance. Start living well with your illness.

This will not happen overnight, however. It takes many small steps, one at a time. A journey that takes a few months for one person may take a year for another. Discover your own pace. Be patient. When you are ready, you will move on. Your life will change for the better.

# ISOLATION

There is one thing you absolutely must understand as you continue your journey. *You are in this alone.* Make no mistake, the only person with the power to change your situation is you. Furthermore, the people you normally rely on for support may not be around for this one. It's not that they don't care. They just don't know what to do. Or how to react. Your pain makes them uncomfortable. They will do whatever they can to avoid facing it, leaving you to confront it alone.

This shocked me. I never realized there was such a stigma attached to pain. I was not prepared for it. It seemed as though the more I needed support from others, the less I received.

It made me angry. I was scared and needed someone to talk to. But no one would listen. It was a complete letdown. Fortunately, in hindsight, I have been able to make sense of it all. I discovered why people react the way they do to pain.

There are two kinds of pain, and they elicit very different responses from people. Acute pain is short-term. It is what a person experiences after surgery or an injury. There are also illnesses which can cause short-term pain. In either case, there is a definite beginning and end to the pain. This makes it easier for people to respond. They know what is expected of them, and for how long. The pain is usually visible (by bandages, a cast or a limp, for example). People are therefore more likely to acknowledge acute pain and offer support to the person suffering from it.

Chronic pain, on the other hand, is long-term and often invisible. One reason for this is that those who suffer from long-term pain develop strong coping mechanisms. They learn how to mask their pain. The more successful a patient is at hiding it, the less support is offered from family and friends. Because the pain does not show, many people fail to realize the patient is, in fact, sick.

When there is no obvious or known cause of pain, it generates skepticism. Such is the case with Fibromyalgia. People can't see the pain, and no one can really explain the origin to them. Doctors don't know what causes FMS. People find it difficult to react to such an unknown. They don't know how, so they dismiss it. Pretend that it doesn't exist. But those who suffer from chronic pain need a solid support system they can count on long-term.

Patients living with chronic illness require more support than most people realize. When someone we know develops a life-threatening illness, we rally around that person. We are very good at supporting others in those situations. By no means do I think Fibromyalgia is more serious than, say, cancer. There is no chance that I will die from FMS. Instead, I have to *live* with it. Every day. But I can't do it alone. I need help.

A support system is especially important during times when the pain is at its worst. There are days when simply getting out of bed is a struggle. Your life becomes closed in, because you are no longer able to do, or interested in doing many of the things you used to do. It is hard to get through the day.

For me, the pain was particularly bad during the months of testing and visiting doctors. We didn't know what was wrong, so we could not begin to treat it. In the meantime, the pain grew in intensity. Nothing we tried in the discovery stage helped with the pain. Now that I am learning to manage my condition, the days of severe pain are fewer and farther between. I still have them, but not as often. Sometimes, I even feel normal again.

Many conditions that cause chronic pain also go into remission for periods of time. During remission, symptoms are greatly diminished, or even absent all together. Suddenly, you feel well again. You can almost forget for a time that you are sick. It is tempting to go back to the life you knew before. You want to celebrate and go a little crazy. You know the illness is not really gone, but you allow yourself to picture what it would be like if it were.

Then you experience a flare-up, and

everything is bad again. Your symptoms grow worse. It can last for hours, days, weeks, even months. You experience anger. Depression. It is a vicious rollercoaster ride. You experience extreme emotional highs followed by extreme lows. It's difficult to keep a positive outlook. Having someone to lean on can make a huge difference. It makes things more bearable.

Fibromyalgia Syndrome is just one of many conditions which cause chronic pain. Because the pain is often not visible, friends and family can ignore it. They convince themselves that it doesn't exist. Chronic pain makes others more uncomfortable than acute pain. People don't know how to react. It's easier to look the other way. Deny the reality of the situation. Some even encourage the patient to conceal the pain.

My pain is invisible, which has proven to be a serious disadvantage. I can't count the times someone has said to me, "Well, you certainly don't *look* sick." I look healthy to other people. They can't see my pain, except perhaps on very bad days when I might move a little slower. My outward symptoms are subtle.

While others may mean it as a compliment, to me there is an implication that I can't really *be* sick if I don't look it. I deeply resent that. I want to scream at people that I have been through the worst imaginable pain, that they have absolutely no idea what it has been like for me. But it wouldn't change anything.

People see a normal person when they look at me. If they didn't already know I was sick, they probably wouldn't guess it. My appearance and health contradict one another. This leads to further isolation. Even people who know of my illness often tend to forget it. They don't think of me as a "sick" person. If I remind them by bringing attention to my health problems, they pull away from me.

Because this happened repeatedly in the early stages of my journey, I tended to retreat into solitude. Isolated myself, to avoid being isolated by others. If I had to go it alone, I thought, at least it would be by my own doing. My own choice. It was easier to accept that way. The only other option was to look at my isolation as being forced, and that was too painful. It was simpler just to say to myself, "You need to be alone." This helped me to adjust my expectations of others, and focus on myself and what I had to do to get well.

Most of the people in my circle of family and friends were aware of my health problems. They knew about all the tests, and even kept track of the growing list of things that were not wrong with me. Throughout the entire process, I thought they understood what I was going through. I thought I could count on them to support me.

Yet most ignored my pain. Separated themselves from me. I watched people physically recoil whenever the subject of my health came up. If I dared mention the word "pain," they would wince. Exchange glances with one another. Try to change the subject. Look anywhere but at me.

The thing that aggravated me most was when someone said, "You should be grateful it wasn't something more serious." That, and "You will be fine" made me livid. I wanted to scream. Of course I was grateful. I realized it could be worse. But that wasn't what mattered to me. I wasn't 'fine.' I was in terrible pain. It was out of control. Why couldn't they see that? Why was it so easy for people to belittle my pain?

I needed to hear from others that the pain was real, and my fears valid. Instead, the people I turned to for support and understanding usually dismissed my pain. They said things like, "It will all just go away one day." That sounds great, I thought to myself, but can I get a guarantee? Of course not. I needed to face my illness head on, not sit around hoping the pain *might* go away someday. I needed to take immediate action. And I felt that no one was willing to help.

It got to the point where I would purposely talk about the pain, just to watch people squirm. I was so bitter. So angry, at the illness, at myself and at the people I felt were abandoning me. I began to take a certain perverse pleasure from making other people uncomfortable. If I wasn't comfortable, why should they be? It wasn't fair. I couldn't give them my pain, of course, but I could do my best to make them hurt in a different way. I struck out at them in anger.

It wasn't mature, and certainly not very considerate. But what exactly did people expect me to say when they asked how I was? Did they really want me to lie? Tell them everything was fine? Didn't they care that I was going through one of the worst times of my life? My pain seemed so obvious. How could they ignore it?

It took some time for me to realize why this was happening. I had to try to understand where my friends and family were coming from. What my experience was like from *their* point of view. I realized that our society does not enable us to deal well with pain. If anything, it teaches us to avoid pain at all costs. For the patient, this is certainly quite difficult. But for those outside the situation looking in, it is not only possible, but preferable to acknowledging it.

As people around me tried to protect themselves, it seemed that everyone was deserting me. It was the first time in my life I felt totally alone. I wasn't looking for sympathy. I didn't want people to feel sorry for me. I needed them to be empathetic, and they weren't. Were they really so uncaring? No, not at all. It was far more complex than that. What I came to realize was that they were hurting, too. Watching me suffer caused them emotional pain.

One day when I was talking to my mom on the phone, she sensed that I was irritated, and asked why. I told her I was upset because she and my dad seemed to ignore my pain. I didn't understand why they wouldn't acknowledge what was happening to me and allow me to talk about it. It had become a taboo subject in their home. But they were my family. Who could I talk to if not them? I needed their understanding.

My mom told me it was too difficult for her, and my dad, to face. They couldn't bear to think about me being in pain, it hurt so much. Seeing their child in pain was like a nightmare they could not escape. They wanted so desperately to "fix it" for me, but knew they couldn't. They felt helpless.

Watching my condition worsen and not knowing why was terrifying for my parents. They were filled with intense fear. They wondered if I might die. Just the sight of me in pain caused them great anguish. My mom began to cry, as she explained their feelings, and it was then that I came to understand.

Suddenly, I understood what my family and friends were going through. I was able to see what it was they needed. I was completely bewildered by it. They were looking for *me* to comfort *them*. They wanted me to hide my pain, so they wouldn't have to face it. They wanted to be reassured that I was going to be alright. But I could not do that, because I didn't know myself what the future held.

How can you possibly care for others when you can barely care for yourself? Offer comfort when you need to receive it? Put on a smiling face when inside you are screaming? You can't. That is the harsh reality. No matter what your friends and family need, your needs are more important at this time.

You need to get well, and you have to do it alone. You cannot waste any of your precious energy making other people feel more comfortable with the situation. This does not mean you don't love them. Nor does it indicate that you are angry. Being angry will only make things more difficult for you. It requires you to exert energy, which you need in order to care for yourself. You have to learn to forgive. Be empathetic to their concern. But don't let it get in the way of your healing. In the long run, they will come to understand.

When you are farther along in your journey, you can re-open the lines of communication. Talk to your friends and family openly about your feelings and needs, as well as theirs. You can begin to deal with the illness together. Define your expectations. Learn to support each other. Be more objective. Your relationships are forever changed, and that calls for a renegotiation. While it may cause temporary strain, your relationships can be restored. They may even become stronger, better than before.

In the beginning, however, as you struggle to accept chronic illness as a permanent part of your life, it's best to tell people you need some time alone. I retreated into a kind of cocoon. Isolated myself on purpose. Made getting well my number one priority. I focused on the pain. Learned to listen to my body's signals, so I could react accordingly and move toward feeling better. I committed myself to the journey.

It was what I needed to do in order to

learn to live with the pain. No one could do it for me. I couldn't expect anyone else to understand what my needs were at that time. How could they? My resentment disappeared as soon as I learned to let them off the hook. I had expected too much. I knew they cared about me, and that meant a great deal. But the journey was mine. I had to go down this unfamiliar road alone.

It will be the same for you. But don't think of this temporary isolation as negative. It can be positive. Time alone is good for body, mind and soul. My mom sent me a card one day, and in it she wrote, "Maybe there is a blessing to be found in this. Now, you *have* to take time out. You have to take care of yourself. Many people consider that a luxury." She was right.

We do often think of time alone, or 'quiet' time, as a luxury. We become so busy we rarely find time just for ourselves. To do the things we like to do. It happened to me. I forgot to do some of my favorite things. Like hiking in the woods with my dog. Taking long, hot bubble baths. Staying in bed on a rainy

Saturday and reading a good book cover to
cover. Listening to classical music over a cup of
herbal tea. Watching sunsets on the beach.
Going to baseball games. Reading the entire
paper, every page, on a lazy Sunday morning.

Before my illness, I had always considered time alone to be sacred. I used to demand
it from myself; a certain amount of time each
week to be alone, doing something I enjoyed.
But lately it had become easier to put personal
time at the bottom of my priority list. There
were too many other commitments and responsibilities. Other things I had to do.

I felt guilty indulging in such a luxury.
Furthermore, I was so consumed by my health
problems that it was difficult to focus on anything else. Even when I could spend time alone,
it was by no means pleasurable. Or satisfying.
The times I was alone were usually spent in bed
or on the floor in my living room, curled up with
a blanket and pillows and the ever-present heating pad. I also spent the great majority of my
time alone trying to sleep. I would toss and turn
for hours, without much success.

Eventually, I made progress. I was able

to nap during the day on weekends. This enabled me to catch a second wind. It was beneficial any weekend, but it was absolutely necessary if I planned to go out in the evening. Before my illness, I had cherished naps. Fibromyalgia gave me an opportunity to discover this simple pleasure anew. And savor it.

Of course, no one wants to be alone all the time. That's not what I am suggesting. I love to spend time with my friends and family. I even value my time with them more as a result of my experience. But I have to prepare for it. The rules of my relationships have changed. Now I can give myself permission to take time out and not feel guilty about it.

It is essential for my health that I make quiet time alone part of my daily routine. This is true for everyone, but it is especially so for people who live with chronic illness. As you have less energy and strength, time becomes more valuable. Be creative with your time management. Ask your spouse to put the kids to bed while you take a bath. Assign household chores to all the members of your family. Be sure to find time just for yourself.

You will find that your priorities change. Because you have less energy, it becomes less important to complete chores (e.g. the beds being made every day or the laundry being folded). Having quality time with your family, or getting out of the house with your friends becomes more important. Because you have less time in which you feel well, you have to make that time count. You learn to spend it doing things you enjoy. This also helps you feel well.

I have established new routines and settled into a "normal" life again, although my perception of what that means has changed. Once I learned to accept my illness, I emerged from my cocoon. I can now explain to my friends and love ones that I am back.

My journey had led me down a secluded path, but now I am on the open road, and I want them to be my travel companions. I have slowly begun to renegotiate my relationships. Learned to trust the people in my life all over again. My bitterness and anger toward the illness are much less intense, although they do surface from time to time.

People are still unsure about my condition. They don't really understand what my illness involves, or how it will affect my relationships with them. But seeing that I am now comfortable makes them feel better, too. I do have to remind them often of my restrictions. But now we can communicate more effectively. It's easier for them to ask questions, and I am up front about my limitations. I also let them know when I need extra encouragement. This is especially important, because you must build a support group, people to rely on when times are tough.

There are official support groups for people with chronic illness. Any type of illness, in fact. I chose not to go this route, however, because a friend whom I trust had some negative experiences with such organizations. I found it was more helpful for me to have friends supporting me than strangers. Even if the strangers did have FMS. This is something you will have to explore for yourself. Your local Yellow Pages, newspapers and hospitals should have a listing of support groups, if you are interested.

Much to my surprise, I discovered that

having people in my workplace know about my illness is a good thing. They are extremely caring and supportive. My co-workers don't make a huge issue of my illness, but they let me know they are aware of it, and are there to support me if I need them. They have even learned to recognize the subtle signs that show I am not feeling well. They always seem to know when I need extra encouragement.

One of my co-workers got into the habit of asking me every morning how I felt. He was looking for clarification. Trying to determine how we were going to interact that day. When I wasn't feeling well, I tended to be quiet, and kept to myself. Sometimes I would be grouchy. But if I was feeling well, I was my usual self, talkative and cheerful. He would 'take my temperature' each morning, as it were, and I appreciated it. It was helpful for both of us.

My parents do the same thing. Knowing me as well as they do, they can sense when my mood changes. Asking how I feel is their way of verifying what they already suspect. Once they know my pain is responsible for my mood, and not something they have done, they can relax.

They also feel more comfortable talking about my condition.

Chronic illness is extremely difficult for many parents to come to grips with. This was true of mine. They had difficulty accepting my condition. This caused me great frustration. After a long struggle, however, my dad finally acknowledged that I have Fibromyalgia. He called to tell me about a special report he saw on the news on the condition. He asked me a few questions about my symptoms. That was progress. He will never know how happy I was when I hung up the phone that day; it was the first time I felt that he was 'with me,' under-standing the reality of my struggle.

It means a great deal to me to know the people I care about are at least making an effort to understand. They never will completely com-prehend what is happening to me, but they don't necessarily have to understand it all in order to support me. What matters is that they care enough to try.

Many of the friends I asked to read this book before I published it came to me and apol-ogized for not handling the situation better.

They felt that they should have cared more, done more. My intent was not to make them feel that way. I told them they had nothing to apologize for. They didn't know any better at the time. But I do appreciate that they are now more aware, and ask how they can be more supportive. Many of my friends have conducted their own research on FMS, in order to have a better understanding of what I face. I have been touched by that.

# REVELATION

The most crucial step in learning to live with the pain associated with a chronic condition is accepting it as part of your everyday life. Up to this point, you and your pain have both been on the defensive, fighting each other. And there have been no winners. If you learn anything at all, it should be that your life simply cannot continue this way. You must move on.

This will be very difficult, and takes time. When I was first diagnosed I was relieved, happy, even excited. I thought my doctors would be able to make me better once they knew what was actually wrong. That was what I wanted: a simple solution. A quick fix, and it was back to the life I knew before. But that was not to be. My life would change in more ways than I could possibly imagine.

The simple truth was this: the pain was here to stay. It was probably never going to go away completely. That took a while to sink in. It seemed so unfair. For months I had been spiraling downward. The pain got worse and worse. I had absolutely no control over it. My fear manifested itself as intense anger and bitterness.

I thought I had to 'defeat' my pain. From my perspective, there needed to be a clear winner. One must be stronger than the other. I thought it was about control. But that was absolutely the wrong way to look at the situation. I lashed out blindly at an enemy I could not see. And I quickly learned there was no way to win this fight. I needed to try a different approach.

So, what *is* the right approach? I believe the only way to successfully live with pain is to treat it as you would a friend. Remember the golden rule: treat others as you want to be treated? Would you treat a friend the way you do your pain? Probably not. Because you have viewed your pain as *the enemy*. Devoted all your strength to fighting it. Refused to accept it. Wanted it to die.

The key to living well with chronic illness is to change the way you view it. Learn to see pain as a friend. You can accomplish your goals more easily if you work together, rather than against each other. You must discard your animosity. Instead, you have to develop a caring relationship with your pain. Build a solid foundation for friendship. Relationships involve give and take. They require nurturing, patience, caring. Mutual respect. Constant attention. You have to work at any relationship, and this is no different.

I suppose you could call this the "if you can't beat 'em, join 'em" approach. I don't like that identification, however, because it implies there is some kind of competition going on. It's not a contest. It is not about winning or losing. It's about living well. In order to do that, you will need to learn to live *with* your pain. Cooperate. Negotiate. Compromise. Work together as a team. This may sound very strange to you, but bear with me.

*You have to make friends with your pain.* Grant it life, rather than deny it. Learn to listen to it. What are its likes and dislikes? What does it want? What does it need? What have you done to make it worse? What can you do to make it better? The answers to these questions are not easily found. But they are part of the process. The more you can learn about your pain, the better off you will be. Let me show you why.

Every week, I negotiate with my pain. In order to make a living, to support myself, I go to work Monday through Friday. I ask my pain to help me make it through the work week. To go into hiding, as it were, so I can do my job. This is difficult for the pain. It requires discipline. I am basically saying that I want to ignore the pain. Asking permission to deny it for a period of time. Why should it let me do this?

The pain gives me what I ask for, because it's confident it will get what it needs in return. It knows it will be rewarded. In exchange for helping me get through the week, I promise to spend the weekend indulging in its needs. I will listen for its signals, and give my body what it wants.

I devote the weekends to caring for my body, to healing the damage sustained during the week. I have learned to let go of expectations, and just "go with the flow." Every weekend is different. Sometimes, my body needs extra rest. Other times it wants to exercise. Whatever it needs, my body always tells me. All I have to do is listen.

This is more complicated than it may sound. I'm still learning to distinguish between the different messages my body sends me. *Pain is the body's signal that something is wrong.* In order for you to determine what, you have to understand its language. Then you and the pain can finally stop fighting each other. You can begin to live well together. Build a strong foundation for a relationship. Define your expectations. Learn to care for each other.

This is exactly what you do when you develop a friendship with another human being. Does it sound absurd? Ask yourself why. The relationship works because both you *and* your pain are recognized. Your body is then able to feel more secure, and doesn't have to take a defensive position.

Remember, your body is being 'attacked' by illness. It needs to know you will do what you can to take care of it. That you will help it maintain the best possible condition. It needs reassurance. Once it receives that, your body will also give up the fight. Declare a cease fire. You can finally begin to live together in *peace*.

As your body communicates with you, many of the signals will be subtle. My physical therapist often talked to me about "good" and "bad" pain. There is a difference. Bad pain is an immediate stop sign. It's a warning that what you are doing will cause harm to your body. It is generally more sharp and intense. Good pain is similar to stretching: it hurts, but you can also sense that your body will benefit from it. Good pain is less severe.

I am trying to learn which is which so I can react appropriately. I have to pay close attention to how my body reacts to certain activities. I don't always know the things I should avoid. But my body gives me signs. Sometimes when I walk, I feel a little sore. If I stop for a bit and stretch, I can usually go on, and I feel good when I finish. When I do something I shouldn't,

I feel serious pain. Unfortunately, the damage has already been done, but I know to avoid that activity in the future.

This is where trial and error comes into play. It is essential. You will learn more about your body's limitations by doing, rather than by *not* doing. Again, you have to let go of your expectations. Adjust your goals. One of my friends who lives with chronic illness told me she prefers to deal with "good intentions."

You will have to test and define the boundaries. It is vital that you educate yourself. Read as much as possible, understanding that not every suggestion (and there will be many) will work for you. Even if you have Fibromyalgia, your boundaries will be different from mine. All I can do is speak from my own experience.

That is why trial and error is so important. Each individual path to wellness is unique. You have to discover your own. It will depend on your condition. You will find that it is often the little, everyday activities that cause so many big problems. And they usually seem inconsequential at first glance.

In the beginning, it seemed other people were more aware of my limitations than I was. Many times, it was the questions people asked that caused me to stop and think, "Should I really do this? What will the consequences be? Am I willing to take the risk? How far can I go before there will be pain?" I had to tread slowly in order to learn. But sometimes I forgot, and forged ahead too quickly.

I am the 'neat freak' in my department at work. So I'm always straightening up our storage area. One day, I was in a cleaning frenzy, carrying things around and not thinking twice about it. My boss came back and said, "Be careful. Don't do too much. If you don't pace yourself, you'll be sorry." He was absolutely right. But I needed that reminder.

My physical therapist reminded me constantly to go slowly and adjust my expectations. My muscles had weakened. Everything that was once firm now jiggled when I walked. I was impatient. I wanted to get back to the shape I was in before the symptoms began. But my body could not do what I wanted it to. No matter how hard I pushed.

Another problem was that the pain was rarely immediate. I would do something I shouldn't, like lift a heavy box, and wouldn't feel the strain for several days. Then I'd wake up in extreme pain. Or lie in bed all night unable to sleep. It was torture. I was exhausted and hurting, but completely unable to sleep. I would toss and turn all night, maybe sleep a few hours, and wake up tired. This often made it very difficult to get through the next day.

I am learning. I still make mistakes. But I view every flare-up as a good experience. Even though I feel bad, I am content. I know I'm making progress. That is important to me. I feel better mentally, knowing how to avoid flare-ups. I am discovering what I need to do to keep the pain from getting out of control. I'm learning to live with my illness. Don't think for a second that I have it all figured out. I haven't. There is no easy solution.

Realizing that my journey will never truly be over was the first step. It's important, because I am not going to wake up one day and suddenly feel normal. At this point, there is no cure for Fibromyalgia. I accept that. But my condition is very manageable, as long as I follow the rules. I continue to learn those rules every day. Each time I face a new challenge, my knowledge expands, and I am able to make adjustments as a result.

Living well with chronic illness requires you to establish new routines. Learn from the past, and look toward the future. You recognize that your life will be different from now on. You accept that. Now you can anticipate positive changes. You can focus on what you need to do to feel well. Your illness will keep you in check. When you are good, you'll be rewarded. When you are bad, your body will punish you.

You will learn to live well with your illness by making friends with your pain. This will give you the tools you need to continue your journey. You are ready to start living well again. Life will be different from now on. But 'different' doesn't have to mean worse. Remember, your perception of "normal" will change. You *can* learn to live successfully with pain. Believe it. Remind yourself every day. Stay positive. There are good times to come.

# LIVING WELL

In order to live well with FMS, after accepting the condition as part of my life, I needed to change my routines. I had to undergo a major overhaul in almost all areas of my life. Most Fibromyalgia patients discover there are things they do on a daily basis which make their pain worse. I needed to discover what activities I could and could not do, and learn to modify my behavior accordingly. This was extremely difficult. As I said before, many of the body's signals are subtle. I am still learning. It's a long process.

I was used to being very active. In addition to working a full time job, I served on several committees and boards, and was rarely at home. I attended meetings two to three nights a week. On weekends, I ran around town doing errands. My social life was also very active. I had very little free time. This hadn't been a problem before I developed FMS.

After the diagnosis, I continued with the things I was used to doing. I expected my body to perform as usual. I pushed it beyond reasonable limits. I then became frustrated and angry when those activities resulted in pain. Sometimes, my body would completely shut down, and I literally could not get out of bed. I now see that my body was trying to protect itself from further harm. It viewed my activity as an attack on its well-being.

Although there is no known cure for most chronic illnesses, many are quite manageable. There are treatment suggestions ranging from traditional to 'New Age'. While a combination of treatments is usually best, each patient has to experiment to find what works best for him or her. I employed several methods in my attempts to live better with Fibromyalgia. Some were successful, others were not. But I tried them all. I had nothing to lose.

## TRADITIONAL MEDICINE

I visit my internist every several months, to evaluate my treatment plan. She often feels my muscles and tests my flexibility. She recently switched me from Elavil to a newer drug, Paxil. There are those who shun prescription drugs, but I'm not one of them. I strongly believe in their use, under the careful supervision of a physician. It is important, however, that the drugs do not mask pain, allowing patients to deny their illnesses.

My medications' primary function is to help me sleep well, as sleeplessness can weaken my ability to cope and function as well as possible. I condone the use of prescription drugs in treating chronic illnesses. Traditional medicine, including prescription drugs, can be very helpful in their management. To treat my Fibromyalgia, I take two drugs as prescribed by my doctor:

**PAXIL** is an anti-depressant, and improves sleep quality by boosting Serotonin levels in the brain. I take it each morning.

**FLEXERIL**, a muscle relaxant, is also used to improve sleep quality. It does this by reducing muscular tightness, pain and fatigue. I take it every night, 60 - 90 minutes before going to bed.

I also take an over-the-counter medication called Aleve sometimes during the day. It helps with the stiffness and discomfort I experience as I sit at my desk, and has no noticeable side effects. Strangely, it is the non-prescription strength of Naproxen, which early on did not seem to help. It does now, and I don't ask questions. I take it on bad days, keeping it in my purse so it is available whenever I need it.

Doctors usually start FMS patients with low dosages, then gradually increase medication until an optimal dosage is determined. It takes trial and error to find the most effective, successful amount and combination of drugs. You must communicate with your doctors about the effects of all medications, negative or positive. Otherwise, you will not discover the appropriate medical way to treat your condition.

My doctor told me what the maximum

dosage was for each of my medications, and gave me permission to experiment until I found what worked best for me. I appreciated her recognition that I knew my body better than anyone else. It was good to have some control. Now I have the freedom to increase or decrease my medications as I see fit. On really bad days I will take extra Flexeril, for example. But I go back to my regular dosage once a flare-up has passed.

Knowing I can change my dosages makes me feel I am taking an active role in the treatment of my condition. I feel more in control. If I can counter a flare-up with extra medicine, I can often keep it under control. In addition, of course, to listening to my body's signals and meeting its needs to feel well. Medicine is *not* a substitute for that. It takes a combination of the two to be successful.

One unavoidable aspect of prescription drugs is side effects. I've had to learn to live with several negative effects, which range from mild to maddening. One is dry mouth. It's very uncomfortable. I feel as though I have cotton in my mouth all the time. I frequently suck on hard candy and drink water or juice. I also chew sugarless gum.

This helps with one of the other side effects - sweet cravings. They are so strong! Even if I'm not hungry, my body will crave chocolate, candy, donuts, or anything with lots of sugar in it. I have to fight these cravings all day long, every day. Unfortunately, I am not always successful, which is one of the reasons I gained weight. But now I try to substitute snacks that taste sweet but are better for me, like fruit or sugar free candy.

The worst side effect I've experienced is severe, painful constipation. It causes me to feel bloated. Many times, I experience pain, tingling and weakness in my buttocks and thighs. The pain is intense, and will not subside until I have had a bowel movement. It can be painful enough that it causes me to cry when I have to go to the bathroom.

It became so severe, I had to see my doctor. She put me on a careful schedule to slowly decrease one of my medications, then the other. It was unclear which of my medications was responsible for the problem. I needed to keep track of how decreasing them affected my regularity and FMS symptoms. She also suggested that I take a fiber supplement, two to three times a day. I was to keep in close contact with her.

After less than two weeks, I was experiencing discomfort. I'd only progressed through the first step of my doctor's plan; I had reduced my Flexeril dosage from 30 mg to 20 mg. It was obvious that the reduced amount was not enough to control my FMS symptoms. I had to resume my regular dosage or face a flare-up.

However, the fiber supplement did make a difference. Eventually, I discovered that this alone was enough. As long as I took two to three doses per day, I remained regular. Forgetting a dose meant that my constipation would return immediately. I had another routine to establish.

Balancing the success of prescription drug treatment and its negative side effects is a very complicated science. Because my medications do help with the FMS symptoms, my doctor doesn't want me to discontinue their use. We discussed other drug possibilities, but agreed it would be taking a gamble to switch. However, when the side effects interfere with my ability to lead a normal life, something must be done.

This is why a close relationship with your physician(s) is vital. I trust my doctor implicitly, and know that she is "on top" of the issues affecting my health. She also trusts my instincts, recognizing that I know my own body better than anyone else. She is open to all my questions, and makes it clear that decisions about the treatment of my condition are mine. I rely on her expertise to help me make those decisions, and am extremely grateful for her professional care and personal concern.

My doctor makes sure I'm aware of other factors which can affect my health. As I mentioned before, I am not supposed to drink alcohol. This is in part because of my medication. Alcohol increases the drowsiness that can come from Paxil. It also decreases the effectiveness of the drug. Furthermore, alcohol robs the body of deep sleep. This is already a problem for people with Fibromyalgia. I don't need to do anything that will make it worse.

The prescription medications I take are designed to assist my body in getting deep, restorative sleep. Drinking alcohol inhibits this.

So, as a general rule, I avoid it. And caffeine. I recently learned that caffeine can remain in your system for up to 24 hours. Occasionally I will break the rules; but I do so knowing there will be consequences.

I understand that I am taking a risk each time I put these substances into my body. I have to weigh the risk against the situation, and decide which is more important. There are times I want to have a drink. I have found that one or two drinks occasionally is OK. But more than can cause serious problems for me.

Recently I allowed myself to be "over-served." I woke up the next day in pain from head to toe. I had never experienced pain quite like it. My entire body hurt. I tried to stretch, but the pain was so severe, it caused me to feel nauseated. I could do nothing but lie still for hours, wondering why I made such a poor choice, while also realizing that "to err is human."

I have erred in planning my medication supply, a costly mistake when managing long-term illness. I use a mail order pharmacy through my company's insurance plan. This allows me to receive three months of medication for the same price I would pay for one month at a traditional pharmacy. I have to pay close attention, however, to how many pills are left. It takes at least a week to receive new medications, so I must order refills in advance.

Recently, I ran out of Paxil. I had not ordered a refill in advance, so I was stuck. After only a few days of not taking it, I was unable to sleep. During a five day period, I slept for no more than six hours. Fortunately, I continued my regular routines for managing my condition, and did not experience any serious pain as a result of my absent-mindedness. But, this was a reminder to me that it takes great discipline to manage a chronic illness; I can't afford to be lax in planning.

I am fortunate that I only take two medications. I have friends who take multiple drugs for their conditions. They have to use special pill organizers and wrist watch alarms to insure that they take the proper amount of medication each day. I just need to remember to take one pill when I awake in the morning and three before bed.

## ALTERNATIVE MEDICINE

Alternative medicine has grown in popularity in the past decade. I found that many people have suggestions on the subject, from acupuncture to yoga. (It's funny how they suddenly want to talk about your condition.) They all have ideas about how to treat your illness. They often know someone who has a chronic illness, so they share what has helped that person. I listen to all the suggestions, and I'll try almost anything once. I read a great deal on methods for managing chronic illness, and decided to try a few.

One method I tried and found to be somewhat successful is fasting. I believe fasting is an effective and safe method of helping your body detoxify itself. It flushes your body of toxins and boosts your immune system. But remember, you should check with your physician before experimenting with any type of alternative medicine.

The first time I tried fasting, I was amazed by the energy I had. After three days of nothing but liquids, I felt refreshed. My pain did not necessarily change during this time, but overall I felt more energetic. I actually felt my body being cleaned out. I didn't experience hunger at all, which was a total surprise.

I fast for five days once a quarter. It's a process, however, that must be followed closely. You have to carefully prepare your body for a week before fasting, and slowly reintroduce food afterwards. I've made the mistake of eating the wrong foods too soon. It caused tremendous pain. My digestive system was not ready. Now, I am more careful, and follow the instructions exactly.

Yoga also seemed like something that could be helpful. Many people recommended it to me. I was willing to give it a try. A co-worker gave me a book for beginners. I took it home and tried some of the positions. But all they did was make my legs fall asleep. I could not sustain any of the positions. So I gave up.

I did, however, take a relaxation therapy class. I learned about deep breathing exercises and meditation, as well as aromatherapy, stretching and massage. I especially liked the deep breathing exercises. I now use them whenever I am feeling stressed, or to wind down at the end of the day. They are especially helpful as a way of getting ready for bed.

Every night, I prepare for sleep. I have a cup of herbal tea, light candles and turn on some relaxing music. I do deep breathing exercises and stretch, taking time do it correctly. I stretch every muscle possible. It usually hurts but feels good at the same time. I tend to be quite stiff by the end of the day. I can't go to bed in that condition, because I will not sleep.

If I am particularly stiff, I will take a hot bath before bed. Muscles stretch more easily when they are warm. The heat of a bath also brings relief from pain. I usually take several baths a week, soaking in very hot water, just to keep from getting too stiff. I feel much better afterwards, and will sometimes take one as soon as I get home from work. Either way, it has become part of a routine I've developed and try to follow every night.

If I decide not to do these things one night, because I was out later than usual, or am too tired to do anything but fall into bed, there will be consequences. My body has come to expect this routine, and rebels when it does not receive it. I am supposed to help my body feel better, not worse. It will remind me if I forget.

My dog has also come to enjoy and expect this nightly ritual, because it often involves her. I will stretch my leg muscles in preparation for our last walk of the day. When we return, I sit cross-legged on one end of the bed and place her on the other. I reach over to rub her belly, stretching many of my muscle groups, including the back, shoulders, buttocks, hips and thighs.

This is an activity we both enjoy. Petting an animal can be extremely therapeutic. I strongly recommend having a pet. The pure, unconditional love they give is like a ray of sunshine in what can be a very dark world for people with chronic illness. They also give you a reason to stay active. No matter how lousy I feel, my dog still needs to be walked.

Dogs are incredibly astute when it comes to sensing emotions. Mine always seems to know when I'm not feeling well. She stays closer to me. Showers me with affection. Doesn't wake me up as early. She seems to understand when the walk is short, and takes great pleasure when it is long. She is learning to adjust, too.

I have tried massage as a means of managing my condition several times. I read only positive things about massage for treating FMS. I even found a massage therapist who is trained to work with FMS patients. But I discovered that while I feel well *during* a massage, I usually don't feel the benefits after it is over.

Once I get off the table, I'm stiff and sore all over again. After a one-hour, full body massage, I expect to feel better. But I don't. Massage doesn't significantly change the way I feel day-to-day. I haven't noticed any long term benefits from this form of treatment, and this has been frustrating.

It might be different if I had one on a regular basis, but my health insurance doesn't cover massage unless it is performed by a physical therapist. My PT doesn't do massage, and I can't afford to have one regularly. I also don't want to change physical therapists. I have a great relationship with mine. If I had seen better results from massage, I may feel differently. For now, I don't see any reason to pursue it.

## NUTRITION

This is the area I have read the most about. There are many different theories on the subject. The perceived effect of nutrition on chronic illness depends on which book you read. There are vastly different opinions. I have read books which swear their special diets will lead to a reduction of symptoms, even cure certain conditions. Others contend that diet has no effect at all on the long term management of chronic illness. It is difficult, as a patient, to know what to believe.

One book I read declared that you could actually be cured of Fibromyalgia. I found this claim interesting. If there is no known cause of FMS, how can you cure it? I was very skeptical. The book provided detailed lists of herbal remedies and vitamin supplements. The problem for me was all the pills I would have to take to follow the plan.

I don't have a problem taking prescription medication, but I do have concerns about taking many different pills. To follow this plan, I would have to take more than thirty pills a day!

Each one had to be bought separately, which would cost a fortune. It was not very appealing.

I never take additional pills without checking with my doctor. I worry about adverse reactions. I won't even take my prescription allergy medicine unless I absolutely have to, because that is just one more pill to put in my body. I call to ask my doctor's permission first. As I researched the many suggested nutritional programs for people with chronic illness, I discovered that they all involved taking large numbers of different pills. I don't want to do that.

I also do not want to go on a complicated diet. I know people who stay on very restrictive diets, and claim they feel better as a result. But following a strict diet does not work well for my lifestyle. It never has. I'm not good at following plans which require food measuring or calorie counting, etc. And most strict diets involve avoiding many different foods.

Instead of following an ultra-restrictive diet, I prefer to follow a few simple rules, which have been successful for me. They are not guidelines from my doctor or a book, although I did take into account certain advice when creating my rules. Most of them are just plain common sense, and do not require any special effort to follow:

- avoid fried and high fat foods
- choose broiled, baked or grilled dishes
- include bran and whole wheat foods
- eat plenty of fresh fruit
- limit red meat to once a week
- watch sugar and salt intake
- limit alcohol and caffeine consumption
- drink three glasses of skim milk daily
- water, water, and more water!

I also take nutritional supplements daily. A co-worker introduced me to supplements which come in a powder form. I now take a vitamin and mineral supplement. It provides 100 percent of the Daily Recommended Values of 25 different vitamins and minerals, as well as several herbs believed to contribute to good health. They are more easily absorbed in this form, and help my body maintain its natural balance. I mix the powder with skim milk, ice and fruit to make a shake twice a day.

There are also special blends for people with health problems. My co-worker uses one for arthritis. I add a special protein powder to my shakes. It's formulated for athletes, but also has many benefits for people with muscle problems, as it reduces muscle fatigue and aids in the recovery and repair process.

The results of these supplements to date have been very positive. The most noticeable change has been in my energy level. I feel much less fatigued during the day as a result of taking the supplements. Or, at least that is my perception. It may just all be in my head. But as a friend recently told me, *"whatever works!"* Simply believing that something helps can actually have that effect. There is nothing wrong with experimenting. If you don't try it, you won't know if it helps.

I plan to continue the use of these supplements long term. They may not make a positive difference, but they won't hurt me, either. I am comfortable taking them regularly. Good nutrition is important for my body, sick or well. Remember, you should contact your own doctor before you make any changes in *your* diet.

## PHYSICAL THERAPY AND EXERCISE

Mild, regular exercise is essential for managing Fibromyalgia Syndrome. When my physical therapist first told me this, I thought he was joking. I laughed. It seemed absolutely ridiculous. How is a person in severe pain supposed to exercise? The very thought of it seemed contradictory. I could barely get up the stairs to my apartment. He understood that, but said I had to learn to work beyond the pain.

He told me to start off slowly, and gradually increase as I began to feel better. He asked me to try walking on a flat surface for ten minutes at first. I could probably do that, I thought. But it didn't seem like 'exercise' to me, considering what I was used to. He had to keep reminding me to adjust my expectations.

This is especially important, because your limitations can change hourly. You can feel well, then suddenly experience pain. Walking for ten minutes was very good for a person in my condition at that point. I was just getting started. My previous views of what constituted exercise would have to change.

I tried to keep that in mind as I began my new, revised exercise program. There were many days when the pain and fatigue made exercise extremely difficult. But I discovered that if I stopped periodically and stretched, it got better. My physical therapist said I should walk for a few minutes first, then stop and stretch. I slowly moved toward twenty minutes of walking, still on a flat surface only. Eventually, I graduated to hills.

FMS patients need to avoid impact activities, like jogging, aerobics or basketball, for example. Walking, swimming and using a stationary bicycle are best. Stretching exercises are also very important. My goal was to recondition my muscles gradually, increasing strength and flexibility. As I continued to meet with my physical therapist, we could see progress in both areas.

I am, however, walking on a tightrope. Overdoing it can cause damage, and even force me to take a step back. But not pushing myself at all will lead to further damage to my muscles. Many FMS patients become inactive as a result of their pain. This causes the pain to increase, as the muscles continue to atrophy. It can be a harmful cycle, and presents a constant challenge. It's easier for me *not* to exercise. So I really have to push myself to do it on a regular basis.

At this point, I have been released from my physical therapist's care. I can call or visit him whenever I need to. But he has given me the foundation I need to stay well. I now understand how to read my body's signals. I know what I can do to stop flare-ups from occurring as often, and to lessen them when they do occur. Most importantly, I am aware of what I need to do to maintain good health.

One of the first and most difficult routines I had to change was my morning ritual. Mild exercise is absolutely essential for managing Fibromyalgia. I need to do it regularly. Yet it is difficult to find the time. I am often too tired to exercise *after* work. So I had to look at my daily schedule and analyze where I might be able to find the time. What could I eliminate?

It turned out there were plenty of things. My morning routine left a lot of extra time. I'm not a morning person, so I used to take a long time to wake up. I would set my alarm for

5:45AM. At 6:15, I would get out of bed and take a shower. Afterwards, I would wrap my head in a towel, fix breakfast and get the paper. I then got back into bed and read the paper while eating breakfast. I'd stay in bed for around 30 minutes. Then I would get up, do my hair and makeup and get dressed.

Obviously, this was a very leisurely routine, and definitely something I could adjust. I decided that instead of reading the paper in bed, I could exercise during that half hour. I canceled my subscription. I purchased a glider machine, which simulates walking. When the weather is bad, I exercise inside. When it's nice, I walk through my neighborhood.

It took a long time, however, to adjust to this routine. I had to take small steps. My body did not want to wake up and exercise. It still wanted to wake up slowly. So I first had to get used to getting out of bed earlier. Then I had to learn to stretch after getting out of bed. Now I try to get up and exercise first, then take a shower and get ready for work. I have to push myself to do it. Exercising is a real challenge for me, and always will be. This is why continuing the routines that make me feel well takes such discipline. It is actually easier to just be in pain. That takes no effort at all.

I usually have breakfast while I am doing my hair and makeup, or after I have arrived at work. The change has been beneficial. Of course I don't always exercise. Some days I just can't. At this point I cannot exercise for thirty minutes; I consider myself lucky if I can go for fifteen. My physical therapist says this is fine. My muscles will strengthen with time. It is a long process, and cannot be rushed. I have to be patient, which as you know by now, I am not. But I'm learning.

Because a friend with a chronic illness recommended yoga so highly, I decided to give it another try. This time I purchased a video. Actually, two videos. One is titled "AM Yoga for Beginners," and the other is "PM Yoga for Beginners." I do find some of the positions uncomfortable, but there is a lot of stretching involved. All areas of the body are involved. Yoga also helps me relax, which is especially good at night. I think I will continue to experiment with it.

## LIFESTYLE CHANGES

Obviously, I had to change my lifestyle in order to live well with my illness. What comes to mind first are social activities. As I mentioned before, weekends are devoted to taking care of my body. I don't go out as much as I used to. I also come home a lot earlier. And I choose different activities. I prefer to go somewhere I can sit and talk with friends, maybe hear some live music.

I have always enjoyed entertaining at home. There, I have more control over the situation. I enjoy 'mellow' evenings now. So, I invite friends to my home more often. Even so, I found that people tend to stand at parties. I'm not sure why this is, but everyone seems to congregate in one area. Now, when I have to take a break from standing, I ask a friend to come sit with me. This keeps me from feeling isolated.

I've also gotten into the habit of taking non-alcoholic beer with me when I go to parties. I have discovered some good non-alcoholic brews. Since all bars serve some type of NA beer, whenever I go out I can have one. I like the taste, and can avoid feeling different.

I have always enjoyed going to movies. But now it is difficult for me to sit through a movie in the theater. I have to move around often, which can be very disturbing to others. Sometimes, I have to stand against the wall for awhile. Now I wait for most movies to come out on video. I rent them and invite friends to come over. I always explain that I need to move around. Most of the time I lie on the floor with pillows, switching from side to side.

One of the biggest changes I have made has been to week-night activities. I used to be away from home as many as four nights a week with volunteer commitments. Now I try to limit my time out to no more than once a week, Sunday through Thursday. Many times, making it through the day is all I can handle.

I prioritize my responsibilities much differently now. My first priority is to stay well. If that means missing a meeting, so be it. I know my commitment to being at that meeting is important, but it is secondary to my health. It has to be. I stay home if I am tired. This helps me feel my best at work. If I don't get enough rest, I will have a difficult time making it through the week.

In a way, I would be violating the agreement I have with pain by going out several nights during the week. It wouldn't be fair to ask permission to make it through the week, and then abuse my body. I have to attempt to limit the damage done during the week, or the pain may rebel. Limiting my activities is the best way to do that.

When I was growing up, my family vacations often included long driving trips. As a result, I tend to drive whenever I go on a trip. I love to drive. I can control when I come and go. I get to see many things I would miss by flying. Also, driving calms me. I would often go for a drive when I was feeling particularly stressed, anxious or angry. But FMS has changed that.

Driving has become a very difficult and uncomfortable activity. Even driving the fifteen minutes to work can cause me pain. I read somewhere that it's important to sit close to the steering wheel, to avoid straining the arms. I adjust my seat so I am sitting straight, with proper back support. I keep my elbows close to my body as I hold the steering wheel. My hips are at a level above my knees. This keeps my body in the best position for driving, minimizing the potential for discomfort.

Driving long distances is a major challenge. But it's a pleasure I refuse to surrender. I still drive to visit friends, as long as they are within a day's drive. Now, I stop frequently to stretch and walk around. I allow more time to get to my destination. I find a driving partner. I try to drive only in daylight, to avoid fatigue (and for safety reasons).

I've made adjustments in my life in order to live well with my illness. Some were drastic, others were not. You will need to experiment with your own changes, to see what works best for you. There will definitely *be* changes. Don't fool yourself about that. Just remember, your limitations and boundaries will be different than mine. Your approach, however, will be similar.

I understood at the onset of my journey that I would have to make concessions. I don't consider them to be "sacrifices." As far as I am concerned, I have not lost anything vital in my attempt to live well with my illness. And while it may have seemed like a major catastrophe to me in the beginning, I now see Fibromyalgia as little more than a ripple on the water. A speed bump, if you will. Warning me to slow down and pay more attention.

## CHANGES IN PROFESSIONAL LIFE

I love my job, and the people I work with. This has been extremely helpful in my struggle to live well with FMS. Having my job to look forward to, and having a strong support group around me each day has been invaluable. Of course, I've had to make adjustments to my professional environment as well.

The first was to rearrange my furniture and work materials at the advice of my physical therapist, so they would be more ergonomic. "Ergonomics" is the science of manipulating an environment for maximum comfort and minimum fatigue. Today, many car companies claim their models are ergonomically designed, because you can reach everything on the dashboard easily, without straining your body.

In terms of the work environment,

ergonomics refers to arranging your work space so that everything you need can be reached comfortably, without placing your body in harmful positions. Your computer screen should be at eye level, and directly in front of you, so you do not have to strain your neck or turn to see it. Your chair should provide proper back support, particularly your lower back. Your desk should not be too high or too low to write on. These are all little ways you can ensure what you do at the office won't irritate or inflame your condition.

I used all of my sick days undergoing tests. Once I was diagnosed, it was obvious that I would require additional time off. I had to apply for sick leave under the Family & Medical Leave Act (FMLA). My record states that I will require "intermittent" days off. Not an extended leave, but a day or two here or there. This enables me to take time off when I am having a flare-up, to take care of myself.

I have not had to miss a substantial amount of work, but I do need an occasional day off (no more than one to two days per month). It's important that my employer know of my condition, and my limitations. It rarely affects my ability to perform my job. But it does sometimes become an issue, as discussed earlier. It is also necessary for my supervisor and I to communicate openly about my condition, and any concerns that may arise on both sides as a result of it.

Because it's difficult to sustain any one position for more than twenty minutes, I save up tasks that require a change. For example, if I have been at my desk typing on the computer for a while, I will get up and fax some papers. I try to divide my day like this, being sure to vary my activities, so I won't become too uncomfortable.

I will often just get up and walk around the office. Some employees take coffee breaks. I take walking breaks. It doesn't affect my job responsibilities, and can actually increase my productivity. Once I've had a short walk I am refreshed, and ready to sit down again and do whatever task needs to be completed.

In a way, my job is well suited for a person with Fibromyalgia. It doesn't involve sitting behind a desk all day long, every day. No two days are the same. Having variety built into my job helps me stay well.

I've noticed lately that I am sometimes forgetful, which I find highly annoying, because I was never that way before. Fortunately, this has not been a serious problem at work, and my boss has a sense of humor about it. He usually laughs at me when he has to repeat instructions and answers to questions. Now I try to write everything down.

One change that may not seem significant, but has been to me, is my professional wardrobe. I can no longer wear high heels. It puts too much of a strain on my legs. From time to time I think I can get away with it, but it always ends in pain. As a matter of fact, I recently wore heels for the first time in months. I was going to a wedding, and wanted to wear my black, three inch 'party shoes'. By the end of the night, I was in terrible pain. I could barely walk for several days.

Over the years, I have accumulated many nice business suits. Not pantsuits, but the real thing, usually with an above the knee skirt. These kinds of suits look ridiculous with flat shoes. They are dressy, and meant to be worn with heels. I have yet to find suitable replacements. I can no longer wear these outfits on an everyday basis. Only for special occasions. The rest of the time, my beautiful suits hang in my closet, unworn.

My professional wardrobe now consists almost exclusively of pants and pantsuits. My shoes all have low heels. I do have a few dresses, which I wear with one or two inch stacked pumps, no higher. The heels must be thick enough to give me the proper support. The focus is on comfort, and not straining my body.

Overall, my condition has not had any serious, negative effects on my professional life. I consider myself fortunate. Many FMS patients are more disabled by the condition. Some are unable to work. I enjoy my career, and am thankful I don't have to give it up as a result of my illness.

## FAITH

I could never have come as far as I have without faith. I know God will take care of me.

I never doubt that.  I sometimes question Him, but I truly believe He will never give me more than I can handle.  I know He watches over me, taking my hand at times to help me over the more difficult bumps in the road.

Feeling His strength, knowing He was there to support me, helped me make the best of my situation.  It gave me the strength I needed to face my challenge.  Most importantly, He did not abandon me in my times of weakness.  It is best expressed by one of my favorite poems, which I have loved since childhood, "Footprints in the Sand:"

*"A man dreamed he was walking
along the beach with the Lord.
Across the sky flashed scenes from his life.
In each scene,
he saw two sets of footprints in the sand:
one was his and the other, the Lord's.
When the last scene flashed before him,
he looked back.
He noticed that at the lowest and
saddest times in his life,
there was only one set of footprints.*

*This bothered him,*
*and he questioned the Lord about it.*
*'You said that if I followed you,*
*you would walk with me all the way.*
*But during my most troublesome times,*
*there is only one set of footprints.*
*Why, when I needed you most,*
*would you leave me?'*
*The Lord replied, 'My precious child,*
*I would never leave you.*
*During your difficult times,*
*when you see only one set of footprints,*
*it was then that I carried you.' "*

- Unknown

I prayed constantly during the testing period. I was so frightened. But I knew I could make it, with His help. God never gives any of us more than we can handle. He knows our limits better than we do, and knows that we gain from all of our experiences. I have learned a great deal from this challenge. I discovered an inner strength I didn't know I had. I learned to slow down and savor each day. I have unearthed many hidden, simple pleasures. They give me the energy I need to move on.

I continue to pray every day for the strength to face my challenges. Each night I thank God for the special beauty of that day. I know I have many blessings in my life, and can't let chronic illness blur my vision or make me negative. Neither can you.

# FACING THE FUTURE

So, everything is great now. All the time. Right? Wrong. I am not perfect. I still make mistakes. The wrong choices. I still have bad days. I have pain. There are days when I hate my illness. I continue to face great challenges every day. I am not always successful at avoiding flare-ups. But I am able to contain them. Pain is my friend. We share the same goals. We work together as a team, to help my body feel as well as it can.

You don't have to give up all the things you enjoy. You just need to make minor adjustments. The key is to be creative. You have to adapt and find new ways to accomplish old

tasks. Chronic illness is the end of a way of life
you knew before. But it is also the beginning of
a new life. One that can be just as satisfying.

Be excited about what is to come.
Develop a new passion for life. If you don't,
nothing I have talked about in this book can ever
help you. You have to remain positive, maintain
reasonable expectations, and nurture your new-
found friendship with pain. It is a delicate relationship, but can stand the test of time with love
and respect.

Life does go on. I have learned to appreciate each moment. Still, there are things I
worry about. I have recurring dreams about
being unable to walk. (I suppose that is a fear I
have deep in my self-conscious) As I look to the
future, there are many other things I am anxious
about:

How will I develop new relationships?

Will I have to hide my pain, in order
for people to draw close to me?

Will men be afraid of my illness?

Will I find someone who appreciates
the strength of my mind and spirit, and
can overlook the weakness of my body?

What about sex? Could it cause pain?

How will pregnancy and childbirth affect
my Fibromyalgia?

Will FMS affect my ability to be a good
mother?

How will having a family affect the
routines which are essential to my health?

Will I feel worse as I get older?

Will I eventually have to move to a
warmer climate, to avoid the negative
effects of cold on my symptoms?

One thing I have often wondered about is
whether I might have to leave St. Louis. Cold
weather has negative effects on my symptoms.
That is common for FMS patients. Last winter

I was going through all the tests, and was constantly in pain. I had nothing to compare it to, so I didn't make the association.

Then I went to Florida on vacation. I felt well for an entire week. It was wonderful. I originally thought that I felt better because I'd left the stress of the experience behind. I always relax on vacation, especially at the beach. But I realized it was the weather the minute I returned to St. Louis. In a split second, as I stepped off the plane and felt a rush of cold air, the pain returned.

I saw the difference in my symptoms a few months later as well. I traveled to Chicago in early May. It was cold and rainy the entire weekend, and I was very uncomfortable. The effects of the cold weather became particularly obvious to me as I sat at Wrigley Field watching a baseball game. Every muscle in my body was tense because I was cold. I was shivering, and in considerable pain. I quickly retreated to the warmth of my hotel room, but the muscle soreness was with me for several days.

If I do decide to relocate, it would be the only major life-changing decision I have made as a result of my illness. It would be a bit of a sacrifice, because I am very happy in St. Louis. Then again, there are other potential reasons I might move in the future: marriage, career, family... I plan to cross that bridge when I come to it.

One strong fear I have concerns raising children. I hope to become a mother some day. I have always looked forward to it. Now, I worry about how it will impact my health, and how FMS might affect my ability to care for my children. I wonder about pregnancy and labor, but it doesn't end there. I would like to nurse my children when the time comes. The feeding schedule, however, would not allow me to have the rest I need. I fear I may be unable to.

A friend of mine who has Fibromyalgia is unable to pick up her baby. She has to have help nearly 24 hours a day. This terrifies me. Recently, I almost dropped a friend's granddaughter. I had lifted her above my head, and had to ask my mother to take her when my arms suddenly gave out.

These are not issues I worry about all the time. There's no point in that. But I do think of them from time to time. Just as FMS has required changes in my present, I recognize that it will impact my future.

In a way, things have come full circle, as they always tend to do. I still face many questions. The difference is, now I have *hope*. I can continue my journey, wherever it may lead me. I am a traveler. And so, now, are you. I wrote this book so you wouldn't have to feel alone. So you could face your illness, knowing others have been where you are now. I hope it will prove to be helpful.

Perhaps our paths will cross one day. If they do, I know we will recognize each other. And we will smile - the kind of empathetic smile that only we can share.

*May the Lord bless you and keep you.*
*May He make His face to shine upon you*
*and give you peace. Now and forevermore.*

# ORDER FORM

TITLE: *Making Friends with Pain: Learning to Live Well with Chronic Illness*
AUTHOR: Elizabeth Flora

**PRICING:**

|   |   |   |
|---|---|---|
| 1-24 | books | $11.95 |
| 25-49 | books | 10.95 |
| 50-74 | books | 9.95 |
| 75-99 | books | 8.95 |
| 100-199 | books | 7.95 |
| 200+ | books | 6.95 |

NAME _____

COMPANY NAME _____

STREET ADDRESS _____

CITY_____ STATE____ ZIP_____

TELEPHONE # _____

SHIPPING: - $4 for the first book, $2 each additional book.
SALES TAX: Please add 7.225% for shipments *to Missouri only.*
TERMS: We accept checks and money orders. Full payment is expected at time of order. (If payment is not enclosed, order will be held).

QUANTITY ____ x $_____ =                     $_____
SHIPPING                                                  $_____
SALES TAX (if applicable)                            $_____
**TOTAL**                                             = $_____

Send order form and payment to:

SADIE BOOKS
9999 Manchester Road, #318
St. Louis, Missouri 63122

# THANK YOU FOR YOUR ORDER!

# RETURN POLICY

1) Our books are returnable. If, for whatever reason, you are unhappy with your purchase, you can return it for a refund.

2) Books damaged in transit are not the responsibility of the publisher. Please make claim to the carrier.

3) To qualify for a refund, returned books <u>must</u> arrive in good, resalable condition.

4) Returns must be accompanied by your packing slip listing quantity, title, author, original invoice number and original invoice date. Books returned with this information will be credited with 100% of the invoice price, minus shipping.

5) Notice of shortage or non-receipt must be made within 30 days of the shipping/invoice date.

6) To package books so they will survive the trip, we recommend you wrap them in the same way that they were sent to you. There are two important steps in successful book packaging: Keep them clean and immobilize them. Place stacked books in a plastic bag. This will separate the packing materials from the book. To keep the books from shifting (which causes scuffing), cut a shipping carton to the right size, or stuff it well with packing materials.

7) Routing: Ship books via parcel post (book rate) prepaid or UPS prepaid to Sadie Books, 9999 Manchester Road #318, St. Louis, MO 63122.